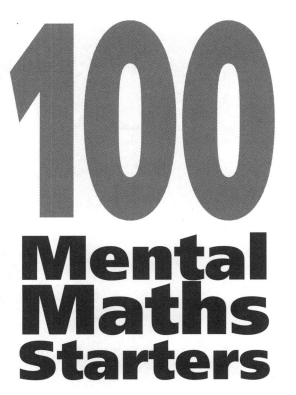

# 100 Mental Maths Starters

## Contents

# Year 4

**Margaret Gronow**

# 100
## Mental
## Maths
## Starters
## Year 4

**Author** Margaret Gronow

**Editor** Joel Lane

**Assistant Editor** David Sandford

**Cover Design** Heather C Sanneh and Clare Brewer

**Series Designer** Paul Cheshire

**Designer** Martin Ford

**Cover photography** Martyn F Chillmaid

**Illustrations** Duncan Scott

## Acknowledgements
The author and publishers wish to thank:

**John Davis and Sonia Tibbatts** for permission to base activities on material in their book 100 Maths Lessons and more: Year 4.

**The Controller of HMSO and the DfEE** for the use of extracts from The National Numeracy Strategy: Framework for Teaching Mathematics © Crown Copyright. Reproduced under the terms of HMSO Guidance Note 8.

Published by Scholastic Ltd,
Villiers House,
Clarendon Avenue,
Leamington Spa,
Warwickshire CV32 5PR
Printed by Bell & Bain Ltd, Glasgow
© **Scholastic Ltd 2002**
**Text © Margaret Gronow 2002**

7890      8901

**British Library Cataloguing-in-Publication Data**
A catalogue record for this book is available from the British Library.

**ISBN 978-0439-01903-3**

## About the series

*100 Mental Maths Starters* is a series of six photocopiable teacher's resource books, one for each of Years 1–6. Each book offers 100 mental maths activities, each designed to last between 5 and 10 minutes. These activities are ideal to start your daily dedicated maths lesson if you are following the National Numeracy Strategy. Each year-specific book provides mental activities for maths within the guidelines of the NNS *Framework for Teaching Mathematics*. The activities can also be used effectively to meet the needs of Primary 1–7 classes in Scottish schools, or classes in other schools functioning outside the boundaries of the National Numeracy Strategy.

This series provides suitable questions to deliver the 'Oral and Mental Starters' outlined in the lesson plans in the companion series from Scholastic, 100 Maths Lessons and more. Reference grids are provided (see pages 4–5) to indicate the lesson and page numbers of the associated lesson plans in the relevant *100 Maths Lessons and more* book. However, the series is also wholly appropriate for independent use alongside any maths scheme of work. The index at the back of each book makes it easy to choose a suitable starter activity for any maths lesson.

Readers of this book who are using *100 Maths Lessons and more: Year 4* will notice that the starters in this book sometimes use different resources or a slightly different method from their counterparts in the cpmpanion book. This is intended to provide greater choice and variety, while keeping to a closely similar mathematical content and progression.

Each book provides support for teachers through three terms of mental maths, developing and practising skills that will have been introduced, explained and explored in your main maths lesson time. Few resources are needed, and the questions for each activity are provided in full. The books are complete with answers, ready for you to pick up and use. In addition, all the activities in the book can be photocopied and the answers cut off to leave activity cards that pupils can work from individually. Alternatively, the activity cards can be used by pairs or small groups, with one child asking questions and the other(s) trying to answer.

The activities are suitable for use with single-ability or mixed-ability groups and single-age or mixed-age classes, as much emphasis has been placed on the use of differentiated and open-ended questions. Differentiated questions ensure that all the children can be included in each lesson and have the chance to succeed; suitable questions can be directed at chosen individuals, almost guaranteeing success and thus increased confidence.

## Learning mental maths

The mental maths starters in this book provide a structured programme with a balanced progression.

They provide regular opportunities for all your pupils to learn, practise and remember number facts. Completed in order, the activities in this book provide the framework of a scheme of work for mental maths practice in Year 4. Several essential photocopiable resource pages are also included (see pages 91–5). To cover the whole year, you will need to add some repeats and/or variations of the activities for consolidation. This book does not provide the groundwork concept teaching for each new skill: that is covered in detail, as the focus of appropriately-timed main teaching activities, in *100 Maths Lessons and more: Year 4* by John Davis and Sonia Tibbatts.

Each activity in this book has one or more learning objectives based on the 'Teaching Programme: Year 4' in the NNS Framework. Key objectives are highlighted in bold. Teacher instructions are provided, stating the particular skills being developed or practised. Discussion of the children's methods is encouraged, since this is essential: it will help the children to develop mathematical language skills; to appreciate that no single method is necessarily 'correct', and that a flexible repertoire of approaches is useful; and to improve their overall confidence as they come to realise that all responses have value. Strategies are encouraged that will enable the children to progress from the known to the unknown number facts, thus developing their ability to select and use methods of mental calculation.

As adults, we probably do maths 'in our heads' more often than we use written methods. Almost without thinking about it, we apply flexible strategies that we developed as children. By following the activities in this series, children will learn to explain their thought processes and techniques – which, in turn, will help them to clarify their thinking and select appropriate methods to use in different contexts.

## About this book

This book is aimed at developing the mental and oral skills of pupils in Year 4/Primary 5. It builds directly on the work of earlier years, covered in the volumes for Years 1, 2 and 3/Primary 2, 3 and 4 in this series.

Emphasis is placed on strategies for addition and subtraction (especially with a total of 100), including adding from the larger number, counting up for a small difference, partitioning, and using doubles or near doubles. There are repeated opportunities to reinforce understanding of place value. The relationships between different times tables are used to support the learning of new tables. Games are included in each term's work to help provide variety and generate enthusiasm for numbers. Open-ended questions are used to challenge the children and extend their thinking.

This book is, first and foremost, a resource for practising teachers. Comments and suggestions from teachers using the book will thus be very welcome, and may be incorporated into future editions.

| 100 Mental Maths Starter | | 100 Maths Lessons | | | |
|---|---|---|---|---|---|
| Starter activity | Activity | Term | Unit | Lesson | Page |
| 1 | reading and writing whole numbers to 1000 | 1 | 1 | 1 | 19 |
| 2 | counting on in repeated steps of 1, 10, 100 | 1 | 1 | 2 | 20 |
| 3 | adding three numbers, finding 10, 9, 11 | 1 | 2–3 | 1 | 24 |
| 4 | adding from larger number (commutative law) | 1 | 2–3 | 2 | 25 |
| 5 | addition: partitioning | 1 | 2–3 | 4 | 26 |
| 6 | addition and subtraction facts to 20 | 1 | 2–3 | 7 | 28 |
| 7 | addition and subtraction facts to 20: using money | 1 | 2–3 | 8 | 29 |
| 8 | subtraction as inverse of addition | 1 | 2–3 | 9 | 29 |
| 9 | counting on and back in steps of 10, 100 | 1 | 4–6 | 2 | 34 |
| 10 | addition and subtraction facts to 20 | 1 | 4–6 | 4 | 36 |
| 11 | counting up for a small difference | 1 | 4–6 | 8 | 37 |
| 12 | identifying near doubles | 1 | 4–6 | 9 | 38 |
| 13 | three-digit doubles and near doubles | 1 | 4–6 | 10 | 38 |
| 14 | pairs: multiples of 5 totalling 100, 1000 | 1 | 4–6 | 11 | 39 |
| 15 | pairs totalling 100 | 1 | 4–6 | 12 | 39 |
| 16 | adding and subtracting near multiples of 10 | 1 | 8 | 1 | 48 |
| 17 | 2, 5, 10 times tables | 1 | 8 | 2 | 49 |
| 18 | dividing by 2, 5, 10 | 1 | 8 | 3 | 50 |
| 19 | 3 and 4 times tables | 1 | 8 | 4 | 50 |
| 20 | dividing by 3 and 4 | 1 | 8 | 5 | 51 |
| 21 | 2, 5, 10 times tables | 1 | 9–10 | 1 | 54 |
| 22 | 3 and 4 times tables | 1 | 9–10 | 2 | 55 |
| 23 | dividing by 2, 5, 10 | 1 | 9–10 | 4 | 56 |
| 24 | dividing by 2, 5, 10 | 1 | 9–10 | 5 | 57 |
| 25 | dividing by 3 and 4 | 1 | 9–10 | 6 | 57 |
| 26 | place value: multiplying by 10 | 1 | 9–10 | 7 | 58 |
| 27 | place value: dividing by 10 | 1 | 9–10 | 8 | 59 |
| 28 | counting up for a small difference | 1 | 11 | 1 | 63 |
| 29 | pairs: multiples of 50 totalling 1000 | 1 | 11 | 4 | 65 |
| 30 | pairs: multiples of 50 totalling 1000 | 1 | 11 | 5 | 66 |
| 31 | adding the nearest multiple of 10 and adjusting | 1 | 12 | 1 | 68 |
| 32 | adding three or four numbers, finding tens | 1 | 12 | 3 | 69 |
| 33 | 5 and 10 times tables | 1 | 12 | 5 | 70 |
| 34 | addition and subtraction facts to 20 | 1 | 13 | 1 | 74 |
| 35 | doubles of numbers to 50 | 1 | 13 | 2 | 74 |
| 36 | halving numbers to 100 | 1 | 13 | 3 | 75 |
| 37 | identifying near doubles | 1 | 13 | 4 | 75 |
| 38 | identifying near doubles | 1 | 13 | 5 | 76 |
| 39 | place value: multiplying by 10, 100 | 2 | 1 | 1 | 83 |
| 40 | adding and subtracting 5, 10, 100 | 2 | 1 | 2 | 84 |
| 41 | addition facts to 20 | 2 | 2–3 | 1 | 88 |
| 42 | adding and subtracting 10, 100, 1000 | 2 | 2–3 | 2 | 88 |
| 43 | missing number: addition and subtraction | 2 | 2–3 | 4 | 90 |
| 44 | missing number: clues from two operations | 2 | 2–3 | 5 | 91 |
| 45 | doubles to 50 | 2 | 2–3 | 6 | 91 |
| 46 | halves of numbers to 100 | 2 | 2–3 | 7 | 93 |
| 47 | addition and subtraction facts to 20 | 2 | 2–3 | 8 | 93 |
| 48 | addition and subtraction facts to 20 | 2 | 2–3 | 9 | 94 |
| 49 | counting on and back in 2s, 4s, 5s | 2 | 4–6 | 1 | 97 |
| 50 | counting on and back in 10s, in 20s, 25s, 50s | 2 | 4–6 | 2 | 98 |

| 100 Mental Maths Starter | | 100 Maths Lessons | | | |
|---|---|---|---|---|---|
| Starter activity | Activity | Term | Unit | Lesson | Page |
| 51 | addition and subtraction of two-digit numbers | 2 | 4–6 | 3 | 98 |
| 52 | addition and subtraction facts to 20 | 2 | 4–6 | 6 | 99 |
| 53 | doubles of tens to 500 and hundreds to 5000 | 2 | 4–6 | 8 | 100 |
| 54 | equivalent addition statements | 2 | 4–6 | 10 | 102 |
| 55 | pairs totalling 100 | 2 | 4–6 | 11 | 102 |
| 56 | recognising shapes from descriptions | 2 | 4–6 | 12 | 103 |
| 57 | matching shapes to descriptions | 2 | 4–6 | 13 | 103 |
| 58 | 2, 3, 4, 5, 10 times tables | 2 | 8 | 1 | 112 |
| 59 | 2, 3, 4, 5, 10 times tables | 2 | 8 | 2 | 112 |
| 60 | 2, 3, 4, 5, 10 times tables | 2 | 8 | 3 | 113 |
| 61 | 2, 3, 4, 5, 10 times tables | 2 | 8 | 4 | 114 |
| 62 | 2, 4 times tables | 2 | 8 | 5 | 115 |
| 63 | 2, 3, 4, 5, 10 times tables | 2 | 9–10 | 1 | 120 |
| 64 | 3, 5, 10 times tables | 2 | 9–10 | 2 | 120 |
| 65 | 3, 5, 10 times tables | 2 | 9–10 | 3 | 121 |
| 66 | 2, 3, 4, 5 times tables | 2 | 9–10 | 4 | 123 |
| 67 | dividing by 2, 3, 4, 5, 10 | 2 | 9–10 | 6 | 123 |
| 68 | dividing by 2, 3, 4, 5, 10 | 2 | 9–10 | 7 | 124 |
| 69 | 6 and 7 times tables | 2 | 9–10 | 9 | 126 |
| 70 | 8 and 9 times tables | 2 | 11 | 1 | 129 |
| 71 | 6, 7, 8, 9 times tables | 2 | 9–10 | 9 | 126 |
| 72 | counting in halves and quarters to 20 | 2 | 11 | 3 | 130 |
| 73 | 7 times table | 2 | 12 | 1 | 132 |
| 74 | 6 times table | 2 | 12 | 2 | 133 |
| 75 | 8 times table | 2 | 12 | 1 | 132 |
| 76 | dividing by 2, 3, 4, 5, 10 | 2 | 12 | 5 | 134 |
| 77 | place value: showing three-digit numbers | 3 | 1 | 1 | 143 |
| 78 | place value: multiplying by 100 | 3 | 1 | 2 | 144 |
| 79 | addition facts to 20: vocabulary | 3 | 2–3 | 1 | 148 |
| 80 | subtraction facts to 20: vocabulary | 3 | 2–3 | 2 | 149 |
| 81 | money: complementary addition to £1.00 | 3 | 2–3 | 8 | 152 |
| 82 | counting on and back in 50s, 100s | 3 | 2–3 | 9 | 153 |
| 83 | adding three numbers: finding 10, 9, 11 | 3 | 4–6 | 3 | 161 |
| 84 | missing numbers: finding 10, 9, 11 when adding | 3 | 4–6 | 4 | 162 |
| 85 | addition and subtraction as inverse operations | 3 | 4–6 | 9 | 164 |
| 86 | addition and subtraction as inverse operations | 3 | 4–6 | 10 | 165 |
| 87 | odd and even numbers | 3 | 4–6 | 11 | 165 |
| 88 | addition and subtraction facts to 20 | 3 | 8 | 1 | 177 |
| 89 | addition facts to 20 | 3 | 8 | 2 | 178 |
| 90 | 6, 7, 8, 9 times tables | 3 | 9–10 | 1 | 183 |
| 91 | doubles of numbers to 50 | 3 | 9–10 | 4 | 184 |
| 92 | halves of numbers to 100 | 3 | 9–10 | 5 | 185 |
| 93 | dividing by 2, 3, 4, 5, 10 | 3 | 9–10 | 6 | 186 |
| 94 | equivalent statements: multiplication, division | 3 | 9–10 | 9 | 188 |
| 95 | doubles: multiples of 10 to 500 | 3 | 11 | 1 | 191 |
| 96 | 6, 7, 8, 9 times tables | 3 | 11 | 3 | 192 |
| 97 | money: cost of more than one item | 3 | 12 | 1 | 197 |
| 98 | multiples: of 6, 7, 8, 9 | 3 | 12 | 2 | 198 |
| 99 | multiples: of 6, 7, 8, 9 | 3 | 13 | 1 | 202 |
| 100 | all times tables | 3 | 13 | 5 | 205 |

# Put up the number

## Starter activity 1

**Resources**
Three sets of numeral cards 0–9 (from photocopiable page 93).

**Objective**
Read and write whole numbers to at least 1000 in figures and words.

**Strategies**
• Divide the class into three groups: 'hundreds', 'tens' and 'units'. Each child has one numeral card. The 0 card will not be needed for the hundreds group.
• Say a two-digit number, for example 43.
• The children holding the correct cards stand together in front of the class to show the number, which the class say together.

| | | | |
|---|---|---|---|
| 1. | 27 | 16. | 476 |
| 2. | 45 | 17. | 723 |
| 3. | 70 | 18. | 399 |
| 4. | 32 | 19. | 535 |
| 5. | 68 | 20. | 658 |
| 6. | 51 | 21. | 260 |
| 7. | 49 | 22. | 807 |
| 8. | 93 | 23. | 185 |
| 9. | 16 | 24. | 612 |
| 10. | 84 | 25. | 979 |
| 11. | 241 | 26. | 321 |
| 12. | 564 | 27. | 736 |
| 13. | 817 | 28. | 498 |
| 14. | 902 | 29. | 144 |
| 15. | 180 | 30. | 853 |

# Stepping stones

1. 25

2. 38

3. 72

4. 54

5. 31

6. 43

7. 29

8. 86

9. 60

10. 57

11. 134

12. 562

13. 428

14. 307

15. 711

16. 396

17. 270

18. 483

19. 519

20. 695

**Starter activity 2**

**Objective**
Count in repeated steps of 1, 10 or 100.

**Strategies**
● Count together in tens from 0 to 100, then in hundreds from 0 to 1000.
● Say each of the numbers shown. The children add 1 and say the answer.
● Repeat for adding 10, then for adding 100.

**Answers**

1. 26, 35, 125
and so on

# Make 10

**Answers**

1. 13
2. 18
3. 15
4. 14
5. 11
6. 16
7. 12
8. 17
9. 19
10. 10
11. 19
12. 11
13. 18
14. 14
15. 12
16. 17
17. 16
18. 11
19. 18
20. 15
21. 15
22. 16
23. 13
24. 17
25. 12

## Starter activity 3

**Objective**
Add three or four small numbers, finding pairs totalling 10, 9 or 11.

**Strategies**
• Stress the idea of finding a pair to make 10, and that changing the order can be useful when adding three or more numbers.

• Find pairs that total 11 or 9.

1. $5 + 5 + 3$
2. $6 + 4 + 8$
3. $2 + 8 + 5$
4. $4 + 9 + 1$
5. $1 + 3 + 7$
6. $8 + 6 + 2$
7. $4 + 2 + 6$
8. $7 + 5 + 5$

9. $7 + 9 + 3$
10. $1 + 0 + 9$
11. $9 + 4 + 6$
12. $5 + 1 + 5$
13. $3 + 7 + 8$
14. $4 + 2 + 8$
15. $1 + 9 + 2$

16. $8 + 3 + 6$
17. $2 + 9 + 5$
18. $4 + 5 + 2$
19. $7 + 6 + 5$
20. $4 + 3 + 8$

21. $3 + 6 + 6$
22. $5 + 7 + 4$
23. $4 + 2 + 7$
24. $8 + 1 + 8$
25. $3 + 4 + 5$

# Think big

1.  6 + 28

2.  8 + 39

3.  7 + 25

4.  9 + 36

5.  8 + 62

6.  7 + 47

7.  9 + 74

8.  4 + 29

9.  8 + 56

10.  9 + 33

11.  7 + 81

12.  5 + 67

13.  6 + 44

14.  9 + 72

15.  4 + 58

16.  20 + 32

17.  40 + 57

18.  33 + 30

19.  50 + 48

20.  25 + 60

## Starter activity 4

**Objectives**
Understand the principle (not the name) of the commutative law as it applies to addition.

**Strategies**
● Remind the children that when adding two numbers, it is usually easier to put the larger number first.

● Give the example 30 + 46 and remind the children to think '46 plus 3 tens'.

### Answers

1.  34
2.  47
3.  32
4.  45
5.  70
6.  54
7.  83
8.  33
9.  64
10.  42
11.  88
12.  72
13.  50
14.  81
15.  62
16.  52
17.  97
18.  63
19.  98
20.  85

Answers

1. 61
2. 62
3. 71
4. 45
5. 62
6. 54
7. 63
8. 83
9. 81
10. 84
11. 93
12. 77
13. 80
14. 72
15. 85
16. 84
17. 62
18. 66
19. 71
20. 66

## Starter activity 5

**Resources**
A board or flip chart.

**Objective**
Partition into tens and units, adding the tens first.

**Strategies**
● Occasionally ask a child to explain the method used.

# Number splits

Write: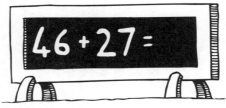

$46 + 27 =$

Ask for the answer and strategies to solve it.
Stress the advantages of partitioning:

$40 + 20$ then $6 + 7 \rightarrow 60 + 13 = 73$
or $46 + 20$ then $66 + 7 = 73$

1.  $26 + 35$
2.  $28 + 34$
3.  $23 + 48$
4.  $19 + 26$
5.  $27 + 35$
6.  $16 + 38$
7.  $34 + 29$
8.  $25 + 58$
9.  $52 + 29$
10. $37 + 47$

11. $36 + 57$
12. $28 + 49$
13. $65 + 15$
14. $43 + 29$
15. $57 + 28$
16. $19 + 65$
17. $36 + 26$
18. $17 + 49$
19. $26 + 45$
20. $38 + 28$

**■SCHOLASTIC**

# Top 20

1. Add 6 and 5 together.

2. 4 + 12

3. 2 + 7

4. double 9

5. 13 + 5

6. 11 + 4

7. 8 + 9

8. 4 + 5

9. What is the total of 3 and 8?

10. double 12

11. 15 + 3

12. 10 plus 7

13. double 19

14. What is 6 more than 9?

15. 5 + 7

16. Add 2 and 13 together.

17. double 8

18. 11 + 6

19. Find the total of 16 and 3.

20. 4 + 9

21. What is 6 more than 7?

22. 9 + 5

23. Add 12 and 7 together.

24. 17 + 3

25. Find the total of 7 and 11.

26. double 14

27. Add 16 to itself.

28. 12 plus 5

29. Find the total of 7 and 8.

30. double 16

**Answers**

1. 11
2. 16
3. 9
4. 18
5. 18
6. 15
7. 17
8. 9
9. 11
10. 24
11. 18
12. 17
13. 38
14. 15
15. 12
16. 15
17. 16
18. 17
19. 19
20. 13
21. 13
22. 14
23. 19
24. 20
25. 18
26. 28
27. 32
28. 17
29. 15
30. 32

**Answers**

1. 17p
2. 12p
3. 19p
4. 15p
5. 9p
6. 7p
7. 4p
8. 14p
9. 7p
10 12p
11. 8p
12. 7p
13. 2p
14. 2p
15. 25p

## Starter activity 7

**Objective**
Consolidate knowing by heart addition and subtraction facts for all numbers to 20, using the context of money.

**Strategies**
● Children raise their hands to answer.

# Adding and subtracting money

1. Add together 12p and 5p.
2. Take 8p from 20p.
3. Find the total of 8p and 11p.
4. I spent 9p and 6p. How much did I spend altogether?
5. How much change would you have from 20p if you spent 11p?
6. Add together 10p and 4p and take 7p from the answer.
7. Buy two pencils costing 8p each. How much change from 20p?
8. I had 6p change from 20p. How much had I spent?
9. Take the total of 7p and 6p from 20p.
10. Add 14p and 5p and take away 7p.
11. Add together 10p, 5p and 2p and take 9p from the answer.
12. I had 8p change from three five pence pieces. How much had I spent?
13. Take the total of 10p, 5p, 2p and 1p from 20p.
14. Buy two apples at 9p each. How much change from 20p?
15. There were 125 pennies in a tin. How much more than £1 was this?

# In the family

1. $7 + 9 = 16$

2. $12 + 8 = 20$

3. $6 + 11 = 17$

4. $15 + 16 = 31$

5. $14 + 9 = 23$

6. $23 + 12 = 35$

7. $28 + 14 = 42$

8. $61 + 28 = 89$

9. $35 + 27 = 62$

10. $26 + 29 = 55$

11. $12 - 3 = 9$

12. $15 - 8 = 7$

13. $24 - 13 = 11$

14. $29 - 15 = 14$

15. $32 - 17 = 15$

16. $41 - 23 = 18$

17. $57 - 36 = 21$

18. $63 - 24 = 39$

19. $38 - 27 = 11$

20. $54 - 36 = 18$

## Starter activity 8

**Objective**
Use the relationship between addition and subtraction.

**Strategies**
● Children raise their hands to say a subtraction fact based on the given addition fact.
● If necessary, write the addition statements on the board.

● Write each subtraction fact on the board. The children say an addition fact based on it.

### Answers

$16 - 9 = 7$

(or $16 - 7 = 9$)

and so on

$3 + 9 = 12$

(or $9 + 3 = 12$)

and so on

## Starter activity 9

**Objective**
● Count on or back in repeated steps of 10 or 100.

# Clap counter

The children count together in tens from the start number. Each time you clap your hands, they reverse the direction of the count.

1. 23

2. 57

3. 11

4. 34

5. 26

6. 32

7. 45

8. 69

9. 30

10. 18

Now they count together in hundreds from the start number.

11. 428

12. 205

13. 512

14. 333

15. 298

16. 149

17. 376

18. 554

19. 187

20. 461

# What am I?

1. I am the total of 5 and 12.
2. I am the total of 6 and 8.
3. I am the difference between 15 and 7.
4. I am the difference between 18 and 3.
5. I am 4, 11 and 5 added together.
6. I am 8, 3 and 6 added together.
7. I am double 6.
8. I am double 9.
9. I am the missing number in $5 + \square + 7 = 20$.
10. I am the missing number in $6 + \square + 3 = 17$.
11. I am half of 10.
12. I am half of 16.
13. I am 4 less than 17.
14. I am 5 less than 11.
15. I am 3 greater than 13.
16. I am 8 greater than 7.
17. My half equals 8.
18. My half equals 12.
19. I am 4 more than double 7.
20. I am 8 more than double 5.

## Starter activity 10

**Objective**
Consolidate knowing by heart addition and subtraction facts for all numbers to 20.

**Strategies**
● Ask quick-fire questions. Children raise a hand to answer.

**Answers**

1. 17
2. 14
3. 8
4. 15
5. 20
6. 17
7. 12
8. 18
9. 8
10. 8
11. 5
12. 8
13. 13
14. 6
15. 16
16. 15
17. 16
18. 24
19. 18
20. 18

# Count up

**Answers**

1. 7
2. 6
3. 5
4. 7
5. 3
6. 7
7. 6
8. 5
9. 5
10. 7
11. 5
12. 6
13. 5
14. 4
15. 6

## Starter activity 11

**Objective**
Find a small difference by counting up.

**Strategies**
• Remind the children that it is often easier to find the difference between two numbers that are close together (eg 205 – 198) by counting up from the smaller number.
• Children raise a hand to answer.

1. Find the difference between 104 and 97.

2. What is the difference between 132 and 126?

3. Take 178 from 183.

4. Take 195 from 202.

5. 101 minus 98

6. 306 minus 299

7. Subtract 188 from 194.

8. Subtract 246 from 251.

9. Find the difference between 117 and 122.

10. Find the difference between 333 and 326.

11. Take 229 from 234.

12. From 413 take 407.

13. From 102 take 97.

14. Take 348 from 352.

15. From 450 take 444.

# Near doubles

Double:

1. 6
2. 13
3. 8
4. 15
5. 7

6. 20
7. 16
8. 9
9. 30
10. 14

Use near doubles:

11. 13 + 12
12. 21 + 19
13. 30 + 32
14. 15 + 14
15. 16 + 17
16. 28 + 30
17. 48 + 49
18. 41 + 42

19. 29 + 31
20. 18 + 19
21. 50 + 60
22. 61 + 62
23. 27 + 25
24. 21 + 18
25. 47 + 48

**Starter activity 12**

**Objective**
Identify near doubles, using known doubles.

**Strategies**
● Start with a quick-fire session to recap known doubles.

● Ask *What is 14 + 15?* to demonstrate using a 'near double' and compensating up or down as necessary.

**Answers**

1. 12
2. 26
3. 16
4. 30
5. 14
6. 40
7. 32
8. 18
9. 60
10. 28
11. 25
12. 40
13. 62
14. 29
15. 33
16. 58
17. 97
18. 83
19. 60
20. 37
21. 110
22. 123
23. 52
24. 39
25. 95

# Near doubles

1. 260
2. 200
3. 240
4. 280
5. 100
6. 300
7. 320
8. 400
9. 800
10. 900
11. 340
12. 380
13. 240
14. 500
15. 220

16. 203
17. 605
18. 101
19. 304
20. 404

## Starter activity 13

**Objective**
Identify near doubles, using known doubles.

**Strategies**
• Encourage the idea that 'double 160' = double 16 tens = 32 tens = 320.

• Recall using 'near doubles' for addition in Starter activity 12.

Double:

| | | | |
|---|---|---|---|
| 1. | 130 | 9. | 400 |
| 2. | 100 | 10. | 450 |
| 3. | 120 | 11. | 170 |
| 4. | 140 | 12. | 190 |
| 5. | 50 | 13. | 120 |
| 6. | 150 | 14. | 250 |
| 7. | 160 | 15. | 110 |
| 8. | 200 | | |

Use near doubles:

| | | | |
|---|---|---|---|
| 16. | 102 + 101 | 19. | 153 + 151 |
| 17. | 303 + 302 | 20. | 201 + 203 |
| 18. | 52 + 49 | | |

# Make 100

1.  80

2.  60

3.  75

4.  45

5.  15

6.  50

7.  35

8.  20

9.  60

10. 30

11. 85

12. 70

13. 90

14. 65

15. 55

16. 800

17. 500

18. 100

19. 400

20. 800

21. 600

22. 200

23. 700

24. 900

25. 300

## Starter activity 14

**Objective**
Derive quickly all number pairs that total 100.

**Strategies**
• Count in 5s and then in 10s to 100 and back again.
• Children raise their hands to say the other one of the pair to total 100, eg *I say 80, you say…* '20.'

• Ask individuals to say the answer and how many steps of 5 they have taken, eg *I say 85, you say…* '15, 3 steps of 5.'

• Ask individuals to find the other number by taking steps of 100 to 1000, eg *I say 800, you say…* '200.'

### Answers

1.  20
2.  40
3.  25
4.  55
5.  85
6.  50
7.  65
8.  80
9.  40
10. 70

11. 15
    (3 steps)
12. 30
    (6 steps)
13. 10
    (2 steps)
14. 35
    (7 steps)
15. 45
    (9 steps)

16. 200
17. 500
18. 900
19. 600
20. 200
21. 400
22. 800
23. 300
24. 100
25. 700

# Make 100

1. 25
2. 42
3. 20
4. 51
5. 34
6. 15
7. 23
8. 6
9. 52
10. 70
11. 37
12. 49
13. 78
14. 83
15. 66
16. 48
17. 71
18. 39
19. 54
20. 87

## Starter activity 15

**Resources**
A board or flip chart.

**Objective**
Derive quickly all number pairs that total 100.

**Strategies**
• Write 100 – 65 = on the board. Ask for the answer and strategies to find it.
• Encourage complementary addition: counting in 'ones', then in groups of 10 (or vice versa).

1. 100 – 75
2. 100 – 58
3. 100 – 80
4. 100 – 49
5. 100 – 66
6. 100 – 85
7. 100 – 77
8. 100 – 94
9. 100 – 48
10. 100 – 30

11. 100 – 63
12. 100 – 51
13. 100 – 22
14. 100 – 17
15. 100 – 34
16. 100 – 52
17. 100 – 29
18. 100 – 61
19. 100 – 46
20. 100 – 13

# Add 10 and adjust

1. 26
2. 35
3. 35
4. 66
5. 78
6. 54
7. 89
8. 61
9. 90
10. 60

11. 19
12. 37
13. 24
14. 52
15. 78
16. 83
17. 61
18. 43
19. 67
20. 20

## Starter activity 16

**Objective**
Add or subtract the nearest multiple of 10, then adjust.

**Strategies**
• Recap: remind the children to add 10, then adjust up or down as necessary.

• Explain that subtracting 9 or 11 can be done in the same way: subtract 10, then adjust.

1. 17 + 9
2. 26 + 9
3. 24 + 11
4. 55 + 11
5. 69 + 9

6. 43 + 11
7. 78 + 11
8. 52 + 9
9. 81 + 9
10. 49 + 11

11. 28 – 9
12. 46 – 9
13. 35 – 11
14. 63 – 11
15. 87 – 9

16. 94 – 11
17. 70 – 9
18. 52 – 9
19. 78 – 11
20. 31 – 11

# Tables Bingo

1. 3 times 2

2. 4 tens

3. double 5

4. 10 times 10

5. 9 times 5

6. 8 twos

7. 7 multiplied by 10

8. 7 times 5

9. 8 tens

10. What is the product of 10 and 5?

11. 5 multiplied by 5

12. 9 times 10

13. 6 fives

14. double 10

15. What is the product of 2 and 4?

16. double 2

17. 1 multiplied by 5

18. 6 tens

19. 6 multiplied by 2

20. double 9

21. 1 times 2

22. 3 fives

23. 2 times 7

## Starter activity 17

**Resources**
Paper and a pencil for each child.

**Objective**
Know by heart multiplication facts for the 2, 5 and 10 times tables.

**Strategies**
● The children choose five numbers from the 2, 5 and 10 times tables and write them spread out on their paper. If they have the answer to a question on their paper, they cross it out. The first child to cross out all five numbers wins.
● Repeat, using the questions in a different order.

### Answers

1. 6
2. 40
3. 10
4. 100
5. 45
6. 16
7. 70
8. 35
9. 80
10. 50
11. 25
12. 90
13. 30
14. 20
15. 8
16. 4
17. 5
18. 60
19. 12
20. 18
21. 2
22. 15
23. 14

# Division quiz

Answers

1. 6
2. 3
3. 4
4. 9
5. 9
6. 7
7. 9
8. 7
9. 10
10. 8
11. 4
12. 6
13. 7
14. 8
15. 5
16. 10
17. 6
18. 5
19. 3
20. 4
21. 2
22. 1
23. 10
24. 3
25. 1

## Starter activity 18

**Objective**
Derive quickly division facts corresponding to the 2, 5 and 10 times tables.

**Strategies**
● Ask: *What is the quotient of 10 and 2?* as a reminder that the 'quotient' is the result of one number being divided by another.

1. How many 2s in 12?

2. Share 15 by 5.

3. 40 divided by 10

4. What is the quotient of 90 and 10?

5. What is half of 18?

6. Share 35 by 5.

7. What is the quotient of 45 and 5?

8. How many 2s in 14?

9. 20 divided by 2

10. How many groups of 5 can I make out of 40?

11. 8 divided by 2

12. 30 divided by 5

13. Share 70 by 10.

14. What is half of 16?

15. How many 5s in 25?

16. Share 50 by 5.

17. What is the quotient of 10 and 60?

18. What is half of 10?

19. 6 divided by 2

20. How many 5s in 20?

21. What is half of 4?

22. How many 2s in 2?

23. 50 divided by 5

24. What is the quotient of 30 and 10?

25. 5 divided by 5

# Tables Bingo

1.   5 times 4

2.   10 multiplied by 3

3.   5 threes

4.   What is the product of 6 and 3?

5.   double 4

6.   7 multiplied by 3

7.   10 times 4

8.   If $9 \times 4 = 36$, what is $36 \div 4$?

9.   If $6 \times 4 = 24$, what is $24 \div 4$?

10.   What is the product of 8 and 4?

11.   3 times 4

12.   8 multiplied by 3

13.   What is the product of 1 and 4?

14.   9 threes

15.   1 multiplied by 3

16.   4 times 4

17.   What is the product of 4 and 7?

18.   9 fours

## Starter activity 19

**Resources**
Paper and a pencil for each child.

**Objective**
**Know by heart multiplication facts for the 3 and 4 times tables.**

**Strategies**
● Repeat the 'Bingo' activity from Starter activity 17. Children write five numbers from the 3 or 4 times tables.
● Questions can be repeated in a different order for a new game.

### Answers

1.   20
2.   30
3.   15
4.   18
5.   8
6.   21
7.   40
8.   9
9.   6
10.   32
11.   12
12.   24
13.   4
14.   27
15.   3
16.   16
17.   28
18.   36

# Division quiz

**Answers**

1. 5
2. 5
3. 1
4. 9
5. 8
6. 4
7. 8
8. 3
9. 2
10. 10
11. 4
12. 2
13. 2
14. 7
15. 4
16. 9
17. 6
18. 1
19. 7
20. 3

## Starter activity 20

**Resources**
A board or flip chart, a pointer.

**Objective**
**Derive quickly division facts corresponding to the 3 and 4 times tables.**

**Strategies**
• Draw a number line on the board. Write the multiples of 3 beneath it as the children chant the 3 times table.
• Say division facts together as they are pointed to at random (for example '27 divided by 3 equals 9').
• Repeat for the 4 times table.
• Ask questions. Children raise their hands to answer.

0   1   2   3   4   5   6   7   8   9   10

1. Share 15 by 3.

2. How many fours in 20?

3. 4 divided by 4

4. If $9 \times 4 = 36$, what is $36 \div 4$?

5. What is the quotient of 24 and 3?

6. Divide 12 by 3.

7. How many fours in 32?

8. Share 9 by 3.

9. 8 divided by 4

10. Divide 30 by 3.

11. Share 16 by 4.

12. How many threes in 6?

13. What is the quotient of 6 and 3?

14. If $7 \times 3 = 21$, what is $21 \div 3$?

15. Divide 40 by 10.

16. How many threes in 27?

17. Share 24 by 4.

18. Divide 3 by 3.

19. How many fours in 28?

20. Divide 12 by 4.

# Times tables facts

1. 4 × 2

2. 10 × 5

3. 3 multiplied by 10

4. What is the product of 2 and 5?

5. double 3

6. What are 4 fives?

7. 5 multiplied by 10

8. multiply 10 by 2

9. 7 × 10

10. double 7

11. What are 6 tens?

12. 7 × 5

13. 1 × 2

14. What is the product of 4 and 10?

15. 8 multiplied by 5

16. double 9

17. 8 × 10

18. 3 multiplied by 5

19. What is the product of 9 and 5?

20. 2 × 10

21. 5 × 5

22. multiply 1 by 10

23. double 8

24. 2 multiplied by 2

25. 5 × 2

26. double 6

27. multiply 10 by 10

28. 1 × 5

29. What is the product of 6 and 5?

30. 9 × 10

## Starter activity 21

**Objective**
Know by heart multiplication facts for the 2, 5 and 10 times tables.

**Strategies**
● A rapid recall test. Children raise a hand to answer.

### Answers

1. 8
2. 50
3. 30
4. 10
5. 6
6. 20
7. 50
8. 20
9. 70
10. 14
11. 60
12. 35
13. 2
14. 40
15. 40
16. 18
17. 80
18. 15
19. 45
20. 20
21. 25
22. 10
23. 16
24. 4
25. 10
26. 12
27. 100
28. 5
29. 30
30. 90

# Times tables facts

**Answers**

1. 12
2. 20
3. 18
4. 4
5. 24
6. 36
7. 27
8. 15
9. 28
10. 3
11. 16
12. 30
13. 40
14. 8
15. 6
16. 32
17. 24
18. 21
19. 12
20. 9

## Starter activity 22

**Objective**
Know by heart multiplication facts for the 3 and 4 times tables.

**Strategies**
• A rapid recall test. Children raise a hand to answer.

1. $4 \times 3$

2. multiply 5 by 4

3. What are 6 threes?

4. $1 \times 4$

5. What is 8 multiplied by 3?

6. multiply 9 by 4

7. $9 \times 3$

8. What are 5 threes?

9. What is the product of 7 and 4?

10. 1 multiplied by 3

11. $4 \times 4$

12. $10 \times 3$

13. What is the product of 10 and 4?

14. What are 2 fours?

15. $2 \times 3$

16. 8 multiplied by 4

17. What are 6 fours?

18. $7 \times 3$

19. What is the product of 3 and 4?

20. $3 \times 3$

**■SCHOLASTIC**

# Division clock

Draw a 'clock face' on the board with the multiples of 5 (up to 50) arranged randomly. The children chant together, moving clockwise around the face, saying each fact twice (eg '30 divided by 5 is 6').

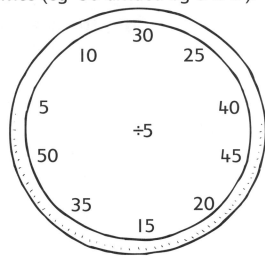

Repeat the activity using multiples of 2, then of 10.

**Starter activity 23**

**Resources**
A board or flip chart, a pointer.

**Objective**
Derive quickly division facts corresponding to the 2, 5 and 10 times tables.

**Strategies**
● Pointing to problematic facts will provide extra practice.

# Division clock

Draw a 'clock face' on the board with the multiples of 3 (up to 30) arranged randomly. Ask the children which times table these numbers are from and how they knew. Point to individual numbers and ask the children to say the relevant division fact (eg '18 divided by 3 is 6').

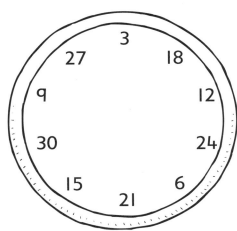

Repeat for division facts from the 4 times table.

**Starter activity 25**

**Resources**
A board or flip chart, a pointer.

**Objective**
Derive quickly division facts corresponding to the 3 and 4 times tables.

# Division Bingo

## Starter activity 24

**Resources**
Paper and a pencil for each child.

**Objective**
Derive quickly division facts corresponding to the 2, 5 and 10 times tables.

**Strategies**
• The children write four numbers between 1 and 10 (inclusive) on their paper. They can cross out each number if it is the answer to a question.
• Repeat the game with the second set of questions.
• Each set of questions could be reused in a different order.

| Game 1 | | Game 2 | |
|---|---|---|---|
| 1. | $25 \div 5$ | 11. | $40 \div 5$ |
| 2. | $18 \div 2$ | 12. | $20 \div 10$ |
| 3. | $10 \div 10$ | 13. | $50 \div 5$ |
| 4. | $35 \div 5$ | 14. | $2 \div 2$ |
| 5. | $20 \div 2$ | 15. | $12 \div 2$ |
| 6. | $4 \div 2$ | 16. | $45 \div 5$ |
| 7. | $30 \div 5$ | 17. | $15 \div 5$ |
| 8. | $40 \div 10$ | 18. | $14 \div 2$ |
| 9. | $16 \div 2$ | 19. | $20 \div 5$ |
| 10. | $30 \div 10$ | 20. | $50 \div 10$ |

# Times 10

1.  $5 \times 10$

2.  $8 \times 10$

3.  $2 \times 10$

4.  $13 \times 10$

5.  $17 \times 10$

6.  $11 \times 10$

7.  $24 \times 10$

8.  $39 \times 10$

9.  $46 \times 10$

10. $72 \times 10$

11. Multiply 58 by 10.

12. $16 \times \square = 160$

13. Make 41 ten times bigger.

14. $34 \times \square = 340$

15. Multiply 50 by 10.

16. $\square \times 10 = 570$

17. What is the product of 56 and 10?

18. Make 65 ten times bigger.

19. How many tens make 480?

20. How many tens make 930?

21. What is the product of 40 and 10?

22. What is the product of 69 and 10?

23. $\square \times 10 = 810$

24. Multiply 73 by 10.

25. What is the product of 10 and 37?

**Answers**

1.  50
2.  80
3.  20
4.  130
5.  170
6.  110
7.  240
8.  390
9.  460
10. 720
11. 580
12. 10
13. 410
14. 10
15. 500
16. 57
17. 560
18. 650
19. 48
20. 93
21. 400
22. 690
23. 81
24. 730
25. 370

# Divide by 10

Answers

1. 4
2. 9
3. 3
4. 12
5. 16
6. 28
7. 45
8. 50
9. 37
10. 71
11. 6
12. 18
13. 24
14. 57
15. 150
16. 11
17. 10
18. 90
19. 640
20. 69
21. 52
22. 76
23. 330
24. 85
25. 48

## Starter activity 27

**Resources**
A board or flip chart.

**Objective**
Use known number facts and place value to divide integers by 10.

**Strategies**
• Write 70 ÷ 10 = 7 on the board. Remind the class that when we divide by 10, the digits move one place to the right.

1. $40 \div 10$

2. $90 \div 10$

3. $30 \div 10$

4. $120 \div 10$

5. $160 \div 10$

6. $280 \div 10$

7. $450 \div 10$

8. $500 \div 10$

9. $370 \div 10$

10. $710 \div 10$

11. Make 60 ten times smaller.

12. Share 180 among 10.

13. What is one tenth of 240?

14. Make 570 ten times smaller.

15. $\square \div 10 = 15$

16. Share 110 among 10.

17. $820 \div \square = 82$

18. What is one tenth of 900?

19. $\square \div 10 = 64$

20. Make 690 ten times smaller.

21. What is the quotient of 520 and 10?

22. Share 760 among 10.

23. $\square \div 10 = 33$

24. What is the quotient of 850 and 10?

25. What is one tenth of 480?

# It's close

1. 21 – 17

2. 30 – 24

3. 42 – 38

4. 74 – 69

5. 51 – 46

6. 23 – 15

7. 65 – 58

8. 82 – 75

9. 54 – 47

10. 100 – 93

11. 105 – 99

12. 111 – 108

13. 276 – 269

14. 433 – 428

15. 500 – 495

16. 302 – 296

17. 886 – 880

18. 501 – 494

19. 725 – 717

20. 603 – 599

## Starter activity 28

**Resources**
A board or flip chart.

**Objective**
Find a small difference by counting up.

**Strategies**
• Write 63 – 58 = on the board. Ask for the answer and strategies to find it.
• Emphasise counting up to subtract when numbers are close together.

### Answers

1. 4
2. 6
3. 4
4. 5
5. 5
6. 8
7. 7
8. 7
9. 7
10. 7
11. 6
12. 3
13. 7
14. 5
15. 5
16. 6
17. 6
18. 7
19. 8
20. 4

# 100 Mental Maths Starters Year4

# Make 1000

Answers

## Starter activity 29

**Objective**
Derive quickly all pairs of multiples of 50 with a total of 1000.

**Strategies**
• Count together in 100s, then in 50s, to 1000 and back again.
• For questions 1–10, ask: *How many more to 1000 from...?*
• Use questions 11–20 for further practice.

1. 200
2. 500
3. 800
4. 400
5. 700
6. 100
7. 600
8. 900
9. 300
10. 150

11. 300
12. 600
13. 200
14. 700
15. 500
16. 900
17. 800
18. 100
19. 400
20. 750

1. 800
2. 500
3. 200
4. 600
5. 300
6. 900
7. 400
8. 100
9. 700
10. 850

11. 1000 take away 700
12. 1000 minus 400
13. By how many is 1000 greater than 800?
14. Subtract 300 from 1000.
15. What's the difference between 500 and 1000?
16. What do I add to 100 to make 1000?
17. 1000 take away 200
18. By how many is 1000 greater than 900?
19. What's the difference between 1000 and 600?
20. 1000 take away 250

# Make 1000

1. 800

2. 750

3. 300

4. 250

5. 450

6. 100

7. 150

8. 550

9. 350

10. 650

11. 1000 minus 850
12. What's the difference between 1000 and 750?
13. By how many is 1000 greater than 400?
14. Take 150 from 1000.
15. Subtract 650 from 1000.
16. 1000 minus 500
17. From 1000 take 950.
18. By how many is 550 less than 1000?
19. What's the difference between 1000 and 700?
20. Subtract 50 from 1000.
21. By how many is 1000 greater than 450?
22. Take 900 from 1000.
23. 1000 minus 250
24. From 1000 take 600.
25. Subtract 350 from 1000.

## Starter activity 30

**Resources**
A board or flip chart.

**Objectives**
Derive quickly all pairs of multiples of 50 with a total of 1000.

**Strategies**
● Write 1000 – 650 = on the board. Ask for the answer and the strategies used (such as complementary addition: adding 50, then steps of 100.)
● For questions 1–10, ask: *How many more to 1000 from…?* Children raise their hands to answer.
● Use questions 11–25 for further practice.

**Answers**
1. 200
2. 250
3. 700
4. 750
5. 550
6. 900
7. 850
8. 450
9. 650
10. 350

11. 150
12. 250
13. 600
14. 850
15. 350
16. 500
17. 50
18. 450
19. 300
20. 950
21. 550
22. 100
23. 750
24. 400
25. 650

**Answers**

# Clever one

## Starter activity 31

**Resources**
A board or flip chart.

**Objective**
Add or subtract the nearest multiple of 10, then adjust.

**Strategies**
• Write 25 + 19 and 33 + 21 on the board. Ask for the answers and strategies to find them.
• Emphasise adding 20 (2 tens), then adjusting up or down as necessary.

1. $26 + 19$
2. $48 + 19$
3. $22 + 19$
4. $37 + 19$
5. $60 + 19$

6. $55 + 19$
7. $49 + 19$
8. $74 + 19$
9. $61 + 19$
10. $33 + 19$

11. $34 + 21$
12. $16 + 21$
13. $42 + 21$
14. $68 + 21$
15. $25 + 21$

16. $51 + 21$
17. $49 + 21$
18. $77 + 21$
19. $30 + 21$
20. $23 + 21$

21. $24 + 29$
22. $48 + 29$
23. $52 + 31$

24. $35 + 31$
25. $27 + 49$

**■SCHOLASTIC**

# Pair up

1. 7

2. 4

3. 9

4. 3

5. 5

6. 2

7. 6

8. 8

9. 1

10. 6 + 4 + 7

11. 3 + 8 + 7

12. 5 + 1 + 9

13. 5 + 5 + 11

14. 4 + 12 + 6

15. 14 + 7 + 3

16. 2 + 13 + 8

17. 9 + 1 + 10

18. 5 + 6 + 4 + 5

19. 3 + 2 + 7 + 8

20. 1 + 6 + 6 + 9

21. 8 + 7 + 5 + 5

22. 7 + 8 + 2 + 6

23. 9 + 9 + 1 + 3

24. 5 + 9 + 7 + 3

25. 4 + 6 + 8 + 9

## Starter activity 32

### Objective
Add three or four small numbers, finding pairs totalling 10.

### Strategies
● Say each number as a question (eg *I say 7, you say...*). The children together say the other number of the pair to total 10.

● Remind the children to make 10 first (if possible) when adding more than two numbers.

**Answers**

1. 3
2. 6
3. 1
4. 7
5. 5
6. 8
7. 4
8. 2
9. 9
10. 17
11. 18
12. 15
13. 21
14. 22
15. 24
16. 23
17. 20
18. 20
19. 20
20. 22
21. 25
22. 23
23. 22
24. 24
25. 27

# Tables Bingo

## Answers

1. 35
2. 90
3. 20
4. 10
5. 5
6. 70
7. 50
8. 40
9. 30
10. 15
11. 45
12. 60
13. 100
14. 80
15. 25

## Starter activity 33

**Resources**
A pencil and paper for each child.

**Objective**
**Know by heart the multiplication facts for the 5 and 10 times tables.**

**Strategies**
• The children write five numbers from the 5 and 10 times tables on their paper. Each number is crossed out when it is the answer to a question.
• The questions could be reused in a different order for subsequent games.

1. 7 times 5

2. 9 multiplied by 10

3. What is the product of 5 and 4?

4. double 5

5. Multiply 5 by 1.

6. What is the product of 7 and 10?

7. half of 100

8. 8 multiplied by 5

9. double 15

10. 3 times 5

11. 9 multiplied by 5

12. What is the product of 10 and 6?

13. 10 times 10

14. double 40

15. Multiply 5 by itself.

# Target number

Ask for any pair of numbers that add together to give a particular number. Collect several for each number.

**Objective**
Consolidate knowing by heart addition and subtraction facts for all numbers to 20.

1.  10

2.  6

3.  14

4.  9

5.  17

6.  3

7.  11

8.  16

9.  5

10.  8

If time allows, ask for number trios to make each target number.

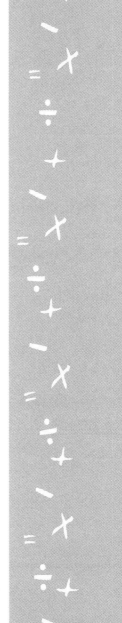

# Double time

Answers

1. 18
2. 28
3. 50
4. 66
5. 84
6. 32
7. 56
8. 96
9. 62
10. 74
11. 24
12. 38
13. 70
14. 100
15. 88
16. 32
17. 98
18. 44
19. 34
20. 52

## Starter activity 35

**Resources**
A board or flip chart.

**Objective**
Derive quickly doubles of all numbers to 50.

Write 'double 27 =' on the board.
Remind the children to use partitioning, or near doubles with adjustment. For example:

$$2 \times 27 = (2 \times 20) + (2 \times 7) = 40 + 14 = 54$$
or $2 \times 27 = (2 \times 25) + (2 \times 2) = 50 + 4 = 54$

1. double 9
2. 2 times 14
3. Add 25 to itself.
4. double 33
5. twice 42
6. double 16
7. Add 28 to itself.
8. double 48
9. 2 times 31
10. 2 times 37

11. Add 12 to itself.
12. double 19
13. twice 35
14. 2 times 50
15. Add 44 to itself.
16. double 16
17. double 49
18. 2 times 22
19. Add 17 to itself.
20. double 26

**SCHOLASTIC**

# Half time

1.  half of 16

2.  half of 17

3.  divide 20 by 2

4.  divide 21 by 2

5.  half of 15

6.  halve 26

7.  halve 70

8.  divide 63 by 2

9.  divide 74 by 2

10.  What is half of 88?

Create a number chain. The children stand in a line or circle. The first child halves the starting number, the next child halves it again, and so on. The child who says a fraction sits down and is 'out' of the game, which continues with a new starting number.

11.  16

12.  24

13.  20

14.  36

15.  52

16.  86

17.  60

18.  32

19.  78

20.  38

## Starter activity 36

**Resources**
A board or flip chart.

**Objective**
Derive quickly doubles of all numbers to 50 and the corresponding halves.

**Strategies**
● Write 'half of 25 =' on the board. Ask for the answer and strategies to find it.
● Emphasise that an odd number halved will always give a fraction.

### Answers

1. 8
2. 8½
3. 10
4. 10½
5. 7½
6. 13
7. 35
8. 31½
9. 37
10. 44
11. 8, 4, 2, 1, ½
12. 12, 6, 3, 1½
13. 10, 5, 2½
14. 18, 9, 4½
15. 26, 13, 6½
16. 43, 21½
17. 30, 15, 7½
18. 16, 8, 4, 2, 1, ½
19. 39, 19½
20. 19, 9½

# Near doubles

## Starter activity 37

**Objective**
Identify near doubles, using known doubles.

**Strategies**
● Ask: *What is 17 + 18?* Demonstrate using 'near doubles' and compensating up (double 17 + 1) or down (double 18 – 1) as necessary.

1. $16 + 15$
2. $20 + 22$
3. $43 + 44$
4. $26 + 25$
5. $11 + 13$
6. $32 + 34$
7. $27 + 29$
8. $49 + 51$
9. $46 + 45$
10. $18 + 16$

11. $21 + 22$
12. $17 + 18$
13. $31 + 29$
14. $35 + 36$
15. $22 + 24$
16. $49 + 47$
17. $16 + 14$
18. $39 + 41$
19. $26 + 24$
20. $18 + 21$

# Near doubles

1. double 50

2. double 100

3. double 80

4. double 75

5. double 110

6. double 90

7. double 60

8. double 400

9. 50 + 49

10. 80 + 81

11. 101 + 100

12. 74 + 75

13. 402 + 401

14. 89 + 90

15. 61 + 60

16. 101 + 99

---

**Starter activity 38**

**Answers**

**Objective**
Identify near doubles, using known doubles.

**Strategies**
● Practise known doubles.

● Encourage the use of near doubles and other strategies to answer these questions. Discuss the methods used for a few of them.

1. 100
2. 200
3. 160
4. 150
5. 220
6. 180
7. 120
8. 800

9. 99
10. 161
11. 201
12. 149
13. 803
14. 179
15. 121
16. 200

---

# Changing position

## Starter activity 39

**Resources**
A board or flip chart.

**Objectives**
Multiply any integer up to 1000 by 10 (whole-number answers) and understand the effect. Begin to multiply by 100.

**Strategies**
• Write 15 in prepared columns headed Th, H, T and U. Ask for a volunteer to multiply this number by 10 and to write the answer in the correct columns beneath.
• Stress that the figures move one place to the left, and the zero is added as a 'place holder'.

• Explain that $15 \times 100 = 1500$. The two 'place holders' are needed because the figures have moved two places to the left.

**Multiply by 10:**

1. 18
2. 40
3. 6
4. 89
5. 135

6. 57
7. 294
8. 603
9. 21
10. 700

**Multiply by 100:**

11. 13
12. 94
13. 5

14. 60
15. 37

# Clap counter

**Starter activity 40**

**Objective**
Count on or back in tens, hundreds or thousands from any whole number up to 10 000.

Count together in 10s up to 200 and back again.
Count in 5s up to 205 and back again.
Count in 100s up to 2100 and back again.

Play 'Clap counter' (see Starter activity 9).

1.  30, add 10

2.  65, add 5

3.  400, add 100

4.  150, take away 10

5.  1800, take away 100

6.  175, take away 5

# Clap counter

**Starter activity 42**

**Objective**
Count on or back in tens, hundreds or thousands from any whole number up to 10 000.

Explain that you are going to play 'Clap counter' (see Starter activity 9). You will say a start number and tell the children the size of the count. They will change the direction of the count each time you clap your hands.

1.  56, add 10

2.  450, 100

3.  170, add 10

4.  1200, add 1000

5.  61, add 10

6.  1600, add 100

# Digit addition

**Answers**

1. 8
2. 4
3. 2
4. 14
5. 7
6. 11
7. 3
8. 5
9. 1
10. 18
11. 9
12. 15
13. 10
14. 16
15. 12
16. 17
17. 0
18. 19
19. 6
20. 13

## Starter activity 41

**Objective**
Consolidate knowing by heart addition and subtraction facts for all numbers to 20.

**Strategies**
● Ask the children to tell you the missing number that will make the target total 20.

1. $5 + 5 + 2 + \square$

2. $3 + 7 + 6 + \square$

3. $4 + 8 + 6 + \square$

4. $2 + 2 + 2 + \square$

5. $4 + 4 + 5 + \square$

6. $5 + 1 + 3 + \square$

7. $6 + 10 + 1 + \square$

8. $9 + 3 + 3 + \square$

9. $8 + 4 + 7 + \square$

10. $1 + 1 + 0 + \square$

11. $2 + 1 + 8 + \square$

12. $3 + 0 + 2 + \square$

13. $5 + 3 + 2 + \square$

14. $1 + 1 + 2 + \square$

15. $4 + 1 + 3 + \square$

16. $1 + 1 + 1 + \square$

17. $8 + 5 + 7 + \square$

18. $0 + 1 + 0 + \square$

19. $2 + 9 + 3 + \square$

20. $2 + 4 + 1 + \square$

# Missing number

1. 4 plus something equals 10

2. 9 plus something equals 12

3. something plus 13 equals 26

4. something plus 18 equals 35

5. 20 minus something equals 13

6. 24 minus something equals 15

7. something minus 8 equals 2

8. something minus 12 equals 13

9. 16 plus something equals 31

10. 49 minus something equals 22

11. something minus 0 equals 29

12. something plus 19 equals 60

13. 17 plus something equals 25

14. something minus 16 equals 4

15. something plus 20 equals 41

16. 39 minus something equals 19

17. 0 plus something equals 27

18. something minus 9 equals 14

19. 12 minus something equals 12

20. something plus 11 equals 36

## Starter activity 43

**Objective**
**Use known number facts and place value to add and subtract mentally, including any pair of two-digit whole numbers.**

**Strategies**
● Say each question, then pause. The children together say the missing number on a silent signal from you (such as a raised hand).

### Answers

1. 6
2. 3
3. 13
4. 17
5. 7
6. 9
7. 10
8. 25
9. 15
10. 27
11. 29
12. 41
13. 8
14. 20
15. 21
16. 20
17. 27
18. 23
19. 0
20. 25

# Which number?

**Answers**

1. 5 and 3
2. 8
3. 9
4. 7 and 5
5. 21
6. 5
7. 11 and 7
8. 20
9. 2 and 6
10. 4 and 5
11. 6
12. 10
13. 7
14. 10
15. 10

**Resources**
A pencil and paper for each child may be useful.

**Objective**
Use known number facts and place value to add and subtract mentally, including any pair of two-digit whole numbers.

**Strategies**
● Work through the first example together. Explain that in a problem of this kind, it is sometimes useful to look at the first rule and list possible outcomes, then see whether any of these satisfy the second rule.

1. My two numbers have a total of 8 and a difference of 2.

2. I am an even number between 5 and 10. I am a multiple of 4.

3. I am an odd number between 4 and 10. I am a multiple of 3.

4. My two numbers have a total of 12 and a difference of 2.

5. I am an odd number between 20 and 26. I am a multiple of 3.

6. If I double this number, the answer is half of 20.

7. The difference between these two numbers is 4. Their sum is 18.

8. I am an even number between 16 and 26. I am a multiple of 5.

9. These two numbers have a sum of 8 and a product of 12.

10. The product of these two numbers is 20. Their difference is 1.

11. If I double this number, the answer is half of 24.

12. If I add 8 to this number, the answer is 18.

13. If I add 5 to this number, the answer is 12.

14. If I take 6 from this number, the answer is 4.

15. If I halve this number and then take away 2, the answer is 3.

**SCHOLASTIC**

# Double number chains

The children stand in a line or circle. The first child doubles the starting number, which is doubled again by the second child, and so on. The game continues until a number greater than 100 is needed. That child sits down and is 'out' of the game, which continues with a new starting number.

1. 4

2. 13

3. 22

4. 3

5. 10

6. 9

7. 15

8. 19

9. 7

10. 17

**Starter activity 45**

**Objective**
Derive quickly the doubles of all whole numbers to 50 and the corresponding halves.

**Answers**
1. 8, 16, 32, 64
2. 26, 52
3. 44, 88
4. 6, 12, 24, 48, 96
5. 20, 40, 80
6. 18, 36, 72
7. 30, 60
8. 38, 76
9. 14, 28, 56
10. 34, 68

# Half number chains

The children stand in a line or circle. The first child halves the start number, which is halved again by the second child, and so on. The child who says a fraction sits down and is 'out' of the game, which continues with a new start number.

1. 80

2. 100

3. 52

4. 64

5. 88

6. 60

7. 72

8. 96

9. 62

10. 56

**Starter activity 46**

**Objective**
Derive quickly the doubles of all whole numbers to 50 and the corresponding halves.

**Answers**
1. 40, 20, 10, 5, 2½
2. 50, 25, 12½
3. 26, 13, 6½
4. 32, 16, 8, 4, 2, 1, ½
5. 44, 22, 11, 5½
6. 30, 15, 7½
7. 36, 18, 9, 4½
8. 48, 24, 12, 6, 3, 1½
9. 31, 15½
10. 28, 14, 7, 3½

# Addition and subtraction facts

**Starter activity 47**

**Objective**
Consolidate knowing by heart addition and subtraction facts for all numbers to 20.

**Strategies**
• Children raise a hand to answer.
• Discuss any vocabulary that is misunderstood.

1. 4 + 3

2. 6 + 8

3. 17 − 12

4. 14 − 11

5. 2 plus 12

6. subtract 9 from 13

7. find the total of 5 and 9

8. from 16 take 11

9. add 8 to 10

10. 6 plus 9

11. find the difference between 15 and 9

12. 7 plus 11

13. 2 plus 0

14. 19 minus 6

15. 12 minus 4

16. subtract 5 from 7

17. add 3 to 15

18. find the total of 11 and 4

19. 10 take 6

20. 4 take 0

21. from 11 take 3

22. 15 plus 4

23. 5 plus 7

24. find the difference between 9 and 7

25. 5 minus 5

26. find the total of 8 and 3

27. 17 add 3

28. 19 minus 15

29. 17 minus 9

30. 6 plus 5

# Addition and subtraction facts

Write these numbers on the board, well spaced out:

**8**        **5**        **2**        **7**

The children work in pairs to make each answer by adding and/or subtracting some or all of these numbers. Discuss the outcomes.

1.  12
2.  11
3.  4
4.  15
5.  0

6.  14
7.  3
8.  20
9.  17
10. 13

**Starter activity 48**

**Resources**
Paper and a pencil for each pair of children; a board or flip chart.

**Objective**
Consolidate knowing by heart addition and subtraction facts for all numbers to 20.

**Answers**

(There is often more than one correct answer.)

1.  7 + 5
2.  8 + 5 – 2
3.  7 – 5 + 2
4.  8 + 7
5.  7 – 5 – 2
6.  7 + 2 + 5
7.  8 – 7 + 2
8.  5 + 7 + 8
9.  8 + 2 + 7
10. 8 + 7 – 2

# Clap counter

Count together:
- in 25s to 400 and back
- in 50s to 1000 and back
- in 20s to 500 and back.

**Starter activity 50**

**Objective**
Extend number sequences formed by counting from any number in steps of constant size.

Play 'Clap counter' (see Starter activity 9), with these starting numbers and instructions.

1.  7, add 10
2.  4, add 20
3.  10, add 50
4.  5, add 25

5.  8, add 50
6.  2, add 20
7.  189, add 10
8.  15, add 25

**Starter activity 49**

**Objective**
Extend number sequences formed by counting from any number in steps of constant size.

**Strategies**
● Divide the class into two groups. Group 1 counts until Group 2 is pointed to, then is quiet while Group 2 carries on. Make frequent changes between groups.

# Number chains

Count in 2s together, forwards and backwards, from...

1.   2 to 60

2.   3 to 71

3.   4 to 100

Count in 5s from...

4.   5 to 100

5.   8 to 68

6.   2 to 82

Count in 4s from...

7.   2 to 70

8.   3 to 55

9.   68 to 100

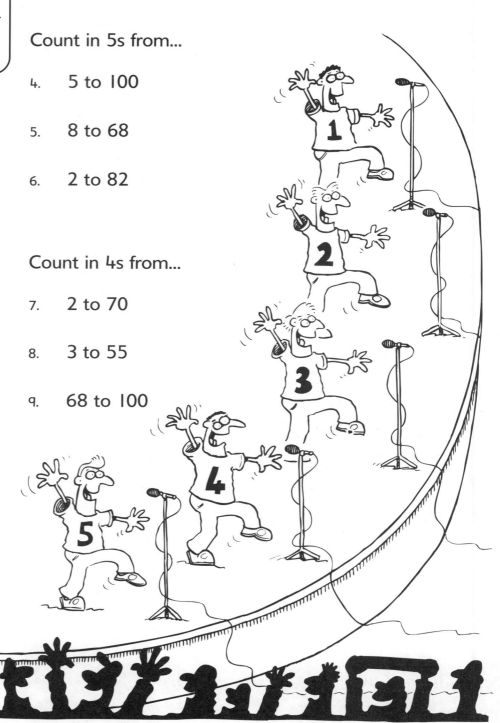

# At speed

1.  17 + 9

2.  11 + 12

3.  18 − 13

4.  50 − 39

5.  24 + 26

6.  35 − 21

7.  48 − 24

8.  22 − 17

9.  61 + 63

10.  25 + 29

11.  81 − 73

12.  48 + 31

13.  64 − 32

14.  45 + 21

15.  84 − 49

## Starter activity 51

**Objective**
**Use known number facts and place value to add or subtract mentally, including any pair of two-digit whole numbers.**

**Strategies**
● Recall various strategies for calculating quickly: the use of near doubles, near multiples of 10, 'counting up', adding from the larger number and so on.
● Children raise a hand to answer.

### Answers
1. 26
2. 23
3. 5
4. 11
5. 50
6. 14
7. 24
8. 5
9. 124
10. 54
11. 8
12. 79
13. 32
14. 66
15. 35

# Number bonds

1.  10

2.  4

3.  15

4.  19

5.  6

6.  2

7.  16

8.  9

9.  5

10.  1

11.  18

12.  14

13.  3

14.  11

15.  7

## Starter activity 52

**Resources**
A board or flip chart.

**Objective**
Consolidate knowing by heart addition and subtraction facts for all numbers to 20.

**Strategies**
● Ask for two volunteers to write an addition or subtraction statement with 8 as the answer.
● Collect several examples for each number, either written or oral.

# Double time

## Starter activity 53

**Resources**
A board or flip chart.

**Objective**
Derive quickly: doubles of multiples of 10 to 500; doubles of multiples of 100 to 5000.

**Strategies**
● As a reminder of a strategy for doubling, write on the board:
$60 \times 2$
$= 6 \text{ tens} \times 2$
$= 12 \text{ tens}$
$= 120$

Double of:

| | | | |
|---|---|---|---|
| 1. | 40 | 11. | 60 |
| 2. | 70 | 12. | 220 |
| 3. | 120 | 13. | 4400 |
| 4. | 300 | 14. | 3900 |
| 5. | 420 | 15. | 150 |
| 6. | 50 | 16. | 280 |
| 7. | 270 | 17. | 20 |
| 8. | 500 | 18. | 140 |
| 9. | 800 | 19. | 4000 |
| 10. | 3000 | 20. | 2600 |

## Starter activity 54

**Resources**
A board or flip chart

**Objective**
Use known number facts and place value to add or subtract mentally, including any pair of two-digit whole numbers.

**Strategies**
● Write on the board:
$28 + 14$
$38 + 4$
$18 + 24$
● Demonstrate that each of these statements is equivalent to, and can be derived from, the others.

# Equation game

Write each example on the board. Ask the children for equivalent statements.

| | | | |
|---|---|---|---|
| 1. | 17 + 23 | 6. | 49 + 16 |
| 2. | 35 + 14 | 7. | 32 + 27 |
| 3. | 26 + 22 | 8. | 24 + 51 |
| 4. | 21 + 48 | 9. | 38 + 25 |
| 5. | 13 + 30 | 10. | 43 + 49 |

# Make 100

1. 70

2. 25

3. 80

4. 88

5. 72

6. 40

7. 10

8. 65

9. 61

10. 41

11. 93

12. 23

13. 58

14. 14

15. 66

16. 27

17. 82

18. 16

19. 99

20. 64

## Starter activity 55

### Objective
Derive quickly all number pairs that total 100.

### Strategies
● Say each number, then pause (eg *I say 70, you say…*). On a silent signal from you, the children together say the other number of the pair to total 100.

### Answers

1. 30
2. 75
3. 20
4. 12
5. 28
6. 60
7. 90
8. 35
9. 39
10. 59
11. 7
12. 77
13. 42
14. 86
15. 34
16. 73
17. 18
18. 84
19. 1
20. 36

**Answers**

1. equilateral triangle

2. triangular prism

3. square

4. regular hexagon

5. cube

6. isosceles triangle

7. square-based pyramid

8. rectangle or oblong

9. cylinder

10. cuboid

## Starter activity 56

**Objectives**
Describe and visualise 3-D and 2-D shapes. Recognise equilateral and isosceles triangles.

**Strategies**
● Ask *What am I?* after each description.

# What's my shape?

1. I am a 2-D shape. I have 3 sides. All my angles are equal, and my sides are the same length.

2. I am a 3-D shape. I will not roll. I have 5 faces. 2 of my faces are triangular and 3 are rectangular.

3. I am a 2-D shape. I am a regular quadrilateral. My sides are of equal length and each of my angles measures 90 degrees.

4. I am a 2-D shape. I am a regular polygon. My 6 sides are of equal length and my 6 angles are equal.

5. I am a 3-D shape. I have 12 edges of equal length, 6 square faces and 8 corners.

6. I am a 2-D shape. I am an irregular polygon. 2 of my 3 sides are equal in length and 2 of my 3 angles are equal in size.

7. I am a 3-D shape. I have 5 faces. 4 of my faces are triangular and my base is square.

8. I am a 2-D shape. I am an irregular polygon with 4 sides. My opposite sides are equal. My 4 angles are right angles.

9. I am a 3-D shape. I can roll. I am made from 2 circles and a rectangle.

10. I am a 3-D irregular polygon. I have 6 faces. My opposite faces are equal. I have 12 edges and 8 corners.

# Shape Snap

Read the shape descriptions from Starter activity 56. The children whose shape matches the description hold their card in the air and say 'Snap'. Ask for the name of the shape.

When all of the shape descriptions have been used, collect the shape cards. Invite a child to take one card from the pile and give clues about the shape. Can the others guess what it is?

**Starter activity 57**

**Resources**
Shape Snap cards (enlarged from photocopiable page 91) – at least one card for each child.

**Objectives**
Describe and visualise 3-D and 2-D shapes. Recognise equilateral and isosceles triangles.

---

# Times tables facts

| | | | |
|---|---|---|---|
| 1. | 90 | 11. | 50 |
| 2. | 4 | 12. | 6 |
| 3. | 27 | 13. | 15 |
| 4. | 35 | 14. | 80 |
| 5. | 14 | 15. | 28 |
| 6. | 18 | 16. | 24 |
| 7. | 60 | 17. | 70 |
| 8. | 32 | 18. | 36 |
| 9. | 25 | 19. | 45 |
| 10. | 8 | 20. | 12 |

**Starter activity 59**

**Objective**
**Know by heart multiplication facts for the 2, 3, 4, 5 and 10 times tables.**

**Strategies**
● Ask: *In which times table is 21 an answer?*
● Explain that 21 is a 'multiple' of 7 and 3 because $7 \times 3 = 21$
● Ask: *Which times tables are these numbers in?* Explain that only the 2, 3, 4, 5 and 10 times tables (up to 10 × each) are allowed.

**Answers**
1. 10
2. 2, 4
3. 3
4. 5
5. 2
6. 2, 3
7. 10
8. 2, 4
9. 5
10. 2, 4
11. 5, 10
12. 2, 3
13. 3, 5
14. 10
15. 4
16. 3, 4
17. 10
18. 4
19. 5
20. 2, 3, 4

# Tables Bingo

**Answers**

1. 21
2. 6
3. 80
4. 20
5. 36
6. 35
7. 9
8. 4
9. 14
10. 60
11. 100
12. 27
13. 2
14. 28
15. 50
16. 15
17. 8
18. 18
19. 25
20. 90
21. 3
22. 12
23. 24
24. 70
25. 16
26. 5
27. 10
28. 40
29. 45
30. 30
31. 32

## Starter activity 58

**Resources**
Paper and a pencil for each child.

**Objective**
**Know by heart multiplication facts for the 2, 3, 4, 5 and 10 times tables.**

**Strategies**
• The children write eight multiples of 2, 3, 4, 5 or 10 from their times tables spread out on their paper. They cross out each number when it is the answer to a question. The first child to cross out all eight numbers wins.
• Repeat the game, using the same questions in a different order.

1. $7 \times 3$
2. $3 \times 2$
3. $8 \times 10$
4. $4 \times 5$
5. $9 \times 4$
6. $7 \times 5$
7. $3 \times 3$
8. $1 \times 4$
9. $7 \times 2$
10. $6 \times 10$
11. $10 \times 10$
12. $9 \times 3$
13. $1 \times 2$
14. $7 \times 4$
15. $10 \times 5$
16. $3 \times 5$

17. $4 \times 2$
18. $9 \times 2$
19. $5 \times 5$
20. $9 \times 10$
21. $1 \times 3$
22. $6 \times 2$
23. $8 \times 3$
24. $10 \times 7$
25. $8 \times 2$
26. $1 \times 5$
27. $5 \times 2$
28. $10 \times 4$
29. $9 \times 5$
30. $10 \times 3$
31. $4 \times 8$

**■ SCHOLASTIC**

# Times tables facts

1.  4 × 3

2.  6 × 5

3.  8 × 2

4.  10 × 10

5.  8 × 4

6.  4 × 2

7.  6 × 10

8.  2 × 5

9.  8 × 3

10. 4 × 4

11. 1 × 10

12. 5 × 3

13. 6 × 2

14. 9 × 5

15. 6 × 4

16. 5 × 5

17. 2 × 2

18. 9 × 3

19. 3 × 10

20. 7 × 4

21. 9 × 2

22. 2 × 3

23. 7 × 10

24. 9 × 4

25. 8 × 5

26. 9 × 10

27. 1 × 4

28. 4 × 5

29. 10 × 2

30. 7 × 3

**Starter activity 60**

**Objective**
Know by heart multiplication facts for the 2, 3, 4, 5 and 10 times tables.

**Strategies**
● A rapid recall test. Children raise a hand to answer.

**Answers**

1.  12
2.  30
3.  16
4.  100
5.  32
6.  8
7.  60
8.  10
9.  24
10. 16
11. 10
12. 15
13. 12
14. 45
15. 24
16. 25
17. 4
18. 27
19. 30
20. 28
21. 18
22. 6
23. 70
24. 36
25. 40
26. 90
27. 4
28. 20
29. 20
30. 21

## Starter activity 61

**Objective**
Know by heart multiplication facts for the 2, 3, 4, 5 and 10 times tables.

**Strategies**
● Write $4 \times 3 = 12$ on the board. Ask for an equivalent multiplication statement (one with the same answer). Examples might include:
$6 \times 2 = 12$
$1 \times 12 = 12$
$3 \times 4 = 12$

# Equation game

Find equivalent multiplication statements to:

1. $4 \times 4 = 16$

2. $10 \times 3 = 30$

3. $10 \times 2 = 20$

4. $3 \times 4 = 12$

5. $6 \times 3 = 18$

6. $10 \times 4 = 40$

7. $5 \times 2 = 10$

8. $6 \times 4 = 24$

9. $5 \times 10 = 50$

10. $50 \times 2 = 100$

11. $2 \times 16 = 32$

12. $7 \times 10 = 70$

13. $2 \times 14 = 28$

14. $9 \times 4 = 36$

15. $6 \times 10 = 60$

# Tables Bingo

1. $9 \times 3$

2. $10 \times 5$

3. $2 \times 10$

4. $2 \times 3$

5. $8 \times 3$

6. $2 \times 4$

7. $10 \times 10$

8. $9 \times 4$

9. $1 \times 5$

10. $10 \times 3$

11. $7 \times 3$

12. $1 \times 2$

13. $5 \times 5$

14. $8 \times 4$

15. $10 \times 7$

16. $3 \times 3$

17. $7 \times 4$

18. $6 \times 10$

19. $3 \times 4$

20. $8 \times 10$

21. $4 \times 4$

22. $5 \times 2$

23. $8 \times 5$

24. $7 \times 2$

25. $9 \times 5$

26. $1 \times 3$

27. $9 \times 10$

28. $3 \times 5$

29. $1 \times 4$

30. $7 \times 5$

31. $6 \times 3$

## Starter activity 62

**Answers**

**Resources**
Paper and a pencil for each child.

**Objective**
**Know by heart multiplication facts for the 2, 3, 4, 5 and 10 times tables.**

**Strategies**
• The children write eight multiples of 2, 3, 4, 5 or 10 spread out on their paper. They cross out each number when it is the answer to a question. The first child to cross out all eight numbers wins.
• Repeat the game, using the same questions in a different order.

1. 27
2. 50
3. 20
4. 6
5. 24
6. 8
7. 100
8. 36
9. 5
10. 30
11. 21
12. 2
13. 25
14. 32
15. 70
16. 9
17. 28
18. 60
19. 12
20. 80
21. 16
22. 10
23. 40
24. 14
25. 45
26. 3
27. 90
28. 15
29. 4
30. 35
31. 18

## Starter activity 63

**Resources**
A board or flip chart, a pointer.

**Objective**
Know by heart multiplication facts for the 2 and 4 times tables.

# Multiplication clock

Draw a 'clock face' as shown below. The children chant each number fact twice as they move around the clock.

Now point at random, asking for a rapid answer each time.

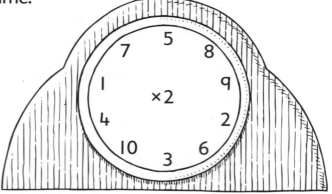

Repeat for the 4 times table, concentrating on the less well known facts.

## Starter activity 64

**Objective**
Know by heart multiplication facts for the 2, 3, 4, 5 and 10 times tables.

**Strategies**
• Ask for an equivalent number statement to each one given (ie one with the same answer). So 4 × 4 is equivalent to 10 + 6, 20 – 4, half 32 and so on.
• The second set of questions require the children to work out the answers in order to find equivalent statements.

# Equation game

1.  $3 \times 2 = 6$

2.  $8 \times 5 = 40$

3.  $10 \times 3 = 30$

4.  $7 \times 2 = 14$

5.  $10 \times 8 = 80$

6.  $9 \times 4 = 36$

7.  $7 \times 3 = 21$

8.  $6 \times 5 = 30$

9.  $2 \times 4$

10.  $3 \times 5$

11.  $10 \times 9$

12.  $8 \times 3$

13.  $9 \times 2$

14.  $10 \times 6$

15.  $8 \times 4$

**■SCHOLASTIC**

# Multiplication clock

Draw a 'clock face' as in starter activity 63 to practise the 5 times table. Repeat for the 10 and 3 times tables.

**Starter activity 65**

**Objective**
Know by heart multiplication facts for the 3, 5 and 10 times tables.

---

## Tables Snap

1. 8 × 2
2. 6 × 5
3. 7 × 3
4. 9 × 4
5. 8 × 5
6. 7 × 2
7. 9 × 3
8. 6 × 2
9. 7 × 4
10. 8 × 3
11. 9 × 5
12. 6 × 3
13. 5 × 5
14. 9 × 2
15. 7 × 5
16. 8 × 4
17. 4 × 5
18. 6 × 4

**Starter activity 66**

**Resources**
Snap cards enlarged from Set 1 (photocopiable page 94) – at least one card per child.

**Objective**
Know by heart multiplication facts for the 2, 3, 4 and 5 times tables.

**Strategies**
● Deal the cards. Those children who have the answer to a question hold up the card and say 'Snap'.
● Finish the activity with rapid answering of all the questions.

**Answers**
1. 16
2. 30
3. 21
4. 36
5. 40
6. 14
7. 27
8. 12
9. 28
10. 24
11. 45
12. 18
13. 25
14. 18
15. 35
16. 32
17. 20
18. 24

**Answers**

1. 3
2. 6
3. 5
4. 1
5. 4
6. 9
7. 2
8. 5
9. 7
10. 8
11. 1
12. 4
13. 7
14. 2
15. 8
16. 5
17. 7
18. 9
19. 3
20. 6

## Starter activity 67

**Resources**
Four or five sets of numeral cards 1–9 (photocopiable page 93).

**Objective**
**Derive quickly division facts corresponding to the 2, 3, 4, 5 and 10 times tables.**

**Strategies**
• Deal about four numeral cards to each child. The children who have the answer to a question hold up the card and say 'Snap'.
• Finish the activity with rapid recall of the answers to all the questions.

# Division Snap

1. How many 5s in 15?

2. How many 2s in 12?

3. divide 20 by 4

4. divide 10 by 10

5. 16 divided by 4

6. 27 divided by 3

7. How many 4s make 8?

8. How many 10s make 50?

9. What is the quotient when 14 is divided by 2?

10. What is the quotient when 40 is divided by 5?

11. divide 3 by 3

12. 8 divided by 2

13. share 70 among 10

14. How many 5s make 10?

15. 32 divided by 4

16. share 15 among 3

17. divide 35 by 5

18. What is the quotient when 90 is divided by 10?

19. divide 9 by 3

20. How many 4s make 24?

# Division Snap

1. divide 20 by 10

2. How many 5s in 25?

3. 21 divided by 3

4. make 80 ten times smaller

5. 4 divided by 4

6. What is the quotient when 12 is divided by 4?

7. How many 5s make 30?

8. 28 divided by 4

9. 45 divided by 5

10. divide 18 by 3

11. How many 3s make 24?

12. What is half of 6?

13. 40 divided by 10

14. How many 5s make 5?

15. 16 divided by 2

16. divide 20 by 5

17. What is the quotient when 60 is divided by 10?

18. What is half of 4?

19. How many 2s make 10?

20. divide 36 by 4

## Starter activity 68

**Resources**
Four or five sets of numeral cards 1–9 (photocopiable page 93).

**Objective**
**Derive quickly division facts corresponding to the 2, 3, 4, 5 and 10 times tables.**

**Strategies**
• Play 'Division Snap' as in Starter activity 67.
• Finish the activity with rapid recall of the answers to all the questions.

### Answers
1. 2
2. 5
3. 7
4. 8
5. 1
6. 3
7. 6
8. 7
9. 9
10. 6
11. 8
12. 3
13. 4
14. 1
15. 8
16. 4
17. 6
18. 2
19. 5
20. 4

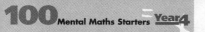

**Resources**
A board or flip chart, a pointer.

**Objective**
Begin to know multiplication facts for the 6 and 7 times tables.

# Number line

Draw a number line on the board:

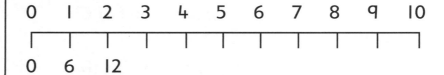

Write the multiples of 6 as the children count from 6 to 60. Discuss the number patterns within the table.

Say the complete table together (eg '1 times 6 is 6'), forwards and backwards.

Explain that several of these facts are already known from the 2, 3, 4, 5 and 10 times tables (eg 5 × 6 = 30) and remove these multiples (6, 12, 18, 24, 30, 60).

Point to numbers along the line at random, with the children saying the whole statement (for example, '5 times 6 is 30').

Repeat for the 7 times table.

# Number line

Draw number lines as for Starter activity 69, but use them to practise the 8 and 9 times tables.

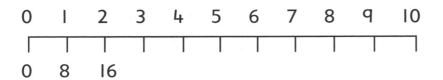

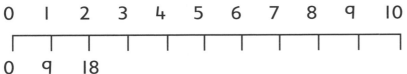

### Starter activity 70

**Resources**
A board or flip chart, a pointer.

**Objective**
Begin to know multiplication facts for the 8 and 9 times tables.

# Multiplication clock

Draw a 'clock face' on the board:

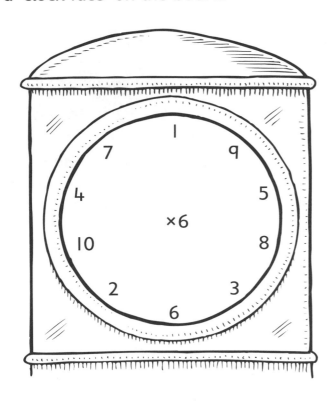

### Starter activity 71

**Resources**
A board or flip chart, a pointer.

**Objective**
Begin to know multiplication facts for the 6, 7, 8 and 9 times tables.

**Strategies**
• The children chant each statement twice as they move around the clock.
• Point at random, with just the answer being given. Concentrate on less well known statements.
• Repeat for the 7, 8 and 9 times tables.
• Remind the children of those facts they already know from other tables.

# Fraction steps

**Starter activity 72**

1. $2\frac{1}{2}$

2. 7

3. $4\frac{1}{2}$

4. $11\frac{1}{2}$

5. 14

6. 20

**Objectives**
Recognise simple fractions that are several parts of a whole; recognise the equivalence of simple fractions.

7. $5\frac{1}{4}$

8. $7\frac{3}{4}$

9. $12\frac{1}{2}$

10. $8\frac{1}{4}$

11. 15

12. $9\frac{1}{2}$

13. $14\frac{1}{2}$

14. $18\frac{1}{2}$

15. 10

16. 17

Count together in halves, then quarters up to 20. Remind the children that $\frac{2}{4} = \frac{1}{2}$

Ask: *When we count in halves, what comes next after...?*

Ask: *What comes next when we count in quarters?*

1.   2

2.   $6\frac{1}{2}$

3.   4

4.   11

5.   $13\frac{1}{2}$

6.   $19\frac{1}{2}$

7.   5

8.   $7\frac{1}{2}$

9.   $12\frac{1}{4}$

10.   8

11.   $14\frac{3}{4}$

12.   $9\frac{1}{4}$

Give the start number and the instruction.

13.   15, take off $\frac{1}{2}$

14.   $18\frac{1}{4}$, add $\frac{1}{4}$

15.   $10\frac{1}{2}$, take off $\frac{1}{2}$

16.   $16\frac{3}{4}$, add $\frac{1}{4}$

■SCHOLASTIC

# 7 times

Write the complete 7 times table as the children say it together. Chant the table forwards and backwards and look at the patterns. Remove the answers of statements already known from other tables (eg 2 × 7 = 14, 5 × 7 = 35). Ask for volunteers to recite the table without looking at the board.

Encourage quick responses, with children raising their hands.

| | | | |
|---|---|---|---|
| 1. | 5 × 7 | 6. | 7 × 7 |
| 2. | 2 × 7 | 7. | 9 × 7 |
| 3. | 6 × 7 | 8. | 1 × 7 |
| 4. | 10 × 7 | 9. | 8 × 7 |
| 5. | 3 × 7 | 10. | 4 × 7 |

If time allows, repeat the questions with all the answers erased from the table.

**Starter activity 73**

**Resources**
A board or flip chart.

**Objective**
Begin to know multiplication facts for the 7 times table.

**Answers**

1. 35
2. 14
3. 42
4. 70
5. 21
6. 49
7. 63
8. 7
9. 56
10. 28

# 6 times

**Answers**

1. 60
2. 18
3. 30
4. 48
5. 6
6. 24
7. 54
8. 36
9. 12
10. 42

## Starter activity 74

**Resources**
A board or flip chart.

**Objective**
Begin to know multiplication facts for the 6 times table.

Write the complete 6 times table as the children say it together. Chant the table forwards and backwards and look at the patterns. Remove the answers of statements already known from other tables (eg 2 × 6 = 12 and 5 × 6 = 30).

Encourage quick responses, with the children raising their hands.

1. 10 × 6
2. 3 × 6
3. 5 × 6
4. 8 × 6
5. 1 × 6

6. 4 × 6
7. 9 × 6
8. 6 × 6
9. 2 × 6
10. 7 × 6

Repeat with all the answers removed.

# 8 times

Repeat Starter activity 74, but use the 8 times table.
Encourage quick responses from individuals.

1. 5 × 8
2. 3 × 8
3. 7 × 8
4. 10 × 8
5. 2 × 8

6. 9 × 8
7. 4 × 8
8. 1 × 8
9. 6 × 8
10. 8 × 8

Repeat with all the answers removed.

## Starter activity 75

**Resources**
A board or flip chart.

**Objective**
Begin to know multiplication facts for the 8 times table.

### Answers
1. 40
2. 24
3. 56
4. 80
5. 16
6. 72
7. 32
8. 8
9. 48
10. 64

---

# Division Snap

1. divide 50 by 10

2. divide 6 by 3

3. How many 3s in 21?

4. How many 10s in 80?

5. 4 divided by 4

6. 20 divided by 5

7. What is the quotient when 36 is divided by 4?

8. What is the quotient when 30 is divided by 10?

9. share 16 between 2

10. How many 3s make 18?

11. divide 24 by 4

12. What is 30 divided by 5?

13. How many 2s make 4?

14. share 24 among 3

15. divide 12 by 3

16. What is 60 divided by 10?

17. divide 5 by 5

18. How many 2s make 20?

19. 12 divided by 4

20. What is the quotient when 45 is divided by 5?

## Starter activity 76

**Resources**
Four or five sets of numeral cards 1–9 (from photocopiable page 93).

**Objective**
**Derive quickly division facts corresponding to the 2, 3, 4, 5 and 10 times tables.**

**Strategies**
● Repeat Starter activity 67 with these questions.

### Answers
1. 5
2. 2
3. 7
4. 8
5. 1
6. 4
7. 9
8. 3
9. 8
10. 6
11. 6
12. 6
13. 2
14. 8
15. 4
16. 6
17. 1
18. 10
19. 3
20. 9

# Put up the number

## Starter activity 77

**Resources**
Four sets of numeral cards 0–9 (from photocopiable page 93).

**Objective**
Read and write whole numbers to at least 10 000 in figures and words, and know what each digit represents.

**Strategies**
● Divide the class into four groups: 'thousands', 'hundreds', 'tens' and 'units'. Give each child one numeral card (the 0 card will not be needed for the 'thousands' group).
● Say a three-digit number, eg 245. The children holding these cards stand together to show the number, which the whole class says.

| | | | |
|---|---|---|---|
| 1. | 16 | 14. | 460 |
| 2. | 74 | 15. | 3512 |
| 3. | 45 | 16. | 6438 |
| 4. | 62 | 17. | 4093 |
| 5. | 38 | 18. | 8126 |
| 6. | 261 | 19. | 1507 |
| 7. | 829 | 20. | 7244 |
| 8. | 193 | 21. | 2673 |
| 9. | 587 | 22. | 9350 |
| 10. | 750 | 23. | 5717 |
| 11. | 375 | 24. | 6582 |
| 12. | 951 | 25. | 8029 |
| 13. | 689 | | |

# Times 100

1. 3 × 100

2. 25 × 100

3. 76 × 100

4. 11 × 100

5. 20 × 100

6. 84 × 100

7. 52 × 100

8. 67 × 100

9. 30 × 100

10. Make 8 a hundred times bigger.

11. 100 multiplied by 14

12. 27 × 10 × 10

13. 10 × 10 × 33

14. 100 multiplied by 49

15. Make 50 a hundred times bigger.

## Starter activity 78

**Resources**
A board or flip chart.

**Objective**
Begin to multiply whole numbers by 100.

**Strategies**
• Mark the board with columns headed H, T, U.
• Ask: *What is 7 × 100?* Write 7 in the units column and ask for a volunteer to write the answer beneath. Stress that because the 7 has crossed two 'boundaries', two 'place holders' are needed.
• Ask individuals to write each answer. The class together say the complete statement (eg '7 times 100 is 700').

### Answers

1. 300
2. 2500
3. 7600
4. 1100
5. 2000
6. 8400
7. 5200
8. 6700
9. 3000
10. 800
11. 1400
12. 2700
13. 3300
14. 4900
15. 5000

# Addition words

## Starter activity 79

**Objective**
Consolidate knowing by heart addition facts for all numbers to 20.

**Strategies**
● Ask for quick responses (to test recall).

1. 3 + 4

2. 14 + 2

3. add 5 and 12 together

4. double 8

5. find the total of 15 and 4

6. What is 7 more than 5?

7. double 9

8. What is 12 greater than 2?

9. 10 + 3

10. What is 8 more than 6?

11. 12 + 5

12. 4 + 9

13. find the total of 9 and 7

14. add 2 and 7

15. add 11 and 6

16. double 7

17. 3 plus 8

18. add 13 and 6 together

19. 8 plus 0

20. 15 + 4

21. 18 + 2

22. add 3 to 14

23. find the total of 7, 3 and 9

24. find the total of 6, 5 and 7

25. 8 plus 6

26. double 5

27. 7 + 0

28. 1 + 14

29. 13 plus 2

30. 16 plus 4

**■SCHOLASTIC**

# Subtraction words

1.  8 – 2

2.  10 – 3

3.  18 minus 5

4.  From 16 take 9.

5.  What is the difference between 13 and 7?

6.  13 – 4

7.  Take 8 from 15.

8.  11 – 2

9.  6 – 0

10. From 9 take 4.

11. From 14 take 5.

12. The difference between 9 and 3.

13. Take 1 from 6.

14. 15 minus 4

15. 20 minus 16

16. Subtract 3 from 18.

17. The difference between 12 and 8.

18. Take 6 from 17.

19. 10 – 2

20. Subtract 3 from 8.

21. 18 – 11

22. How much less than 17 is 15?

23. 18 minus 12

24. How much less than 19 is 14?

25. From 15 take 3.

26. How much greater than 9 is 17?

27. The difference between 7 and 0.

28. 18 – 4

29. How much greater than 2 is 19?

30. 12 – 7

## Starter activity 80

**Objective**
Consolidate knowing by heart subtraction facts for all numbers to 20.

**Strategies**
• Ask for quick responses.

### Answers

1. 6
2. 7
3. 13
4. 7
5. 6
6. 9
7. 7
8. 9
9. 6
10. 5
11. 9
12. 6
13. 5
14. 11
15. 4
16. 15
17. 4
18. 11
19. 8
20. 5
21. 7
22. 2
23. 6
24. 5
25. 12
26. 8
27. 7
28. 14
29. 17
30. 5

# Make £1.00

**Answers**

1. 100
2. 50
3. 10
4. 20
5. 5
6. 2

7. 50p
8. 30p
9. 80p
10. 35p
11. 60p
12. 18p
13. 25p
14. 90p
15. 32p
16. 45p
17. 64p
18. 8p
19. 40p
20. 61p

**Starter activity 81**

**Objective**
Derive quickly all number pairs that total 100.

**Strategies**
● For questions 7–20, encourage the use of complementary addition.

Ask for coin names up to £1.00.

The children raise their hands to answer questions.

1.  How many 1p coins are equal to £1.00?

2.  How many 2p coins in £1.00?

3.  How many 10p coins in £1.00?

4.  How many 5p coins in £1.00?

5.  How many 20p coins in £1.00?

6.  How many 50p coins in £1.00?

Ask: How much more do I need to reach £1.00 from...?

| | | | |
|---|---|---|---|
| 7. | 50p | 14. | 10p |
| 8. | 70p | 15. | 68p |
| 9. | 20p | 16. | 55p |
| 10. | 65p | 17. | 36p |
| 11. | 40p | 18. | 92p |
| 12. | 82p | 19. | 60p |
| 13. | 75p | 20. | 39p |

**◾SCHOLASTIC**

# Clap counter

**Objective**
Count on or back in repeated steps of 100.

The children count in 100s from the start number. When you clap your hands, the children reverse the direction of the count. Include several changes of direction each time.

Start numbers:

1.  0

2.  125

3.  217

4.  652

5.  189

6.  2765

7.  1438

8.  873

Now ask the children to count in 50s from:

9.  150

10.  125

11.  180

12.  205

# Make 10

**Answers**

**Starter activity 83**

**Objective**
Add three or four small numbers, finding pairs totalling 10, 9 or 11.

Ask for all pairs of numbers with a total of 10.

Find the 10, then the answer:

| | | | |
|---|---|---|---|
| 1. | 6 + 4 + 8 | 4. | 1 + 3 + 9 |
| 2. | 3 + 2 + 7 | 5. | 6 + 4 + 6 |
| 3. | 9 + 5 + 5 | 6. | 7 + 3 + 4 |

Find the 9, then the answer (add 10 and adjust):

| | | | |
|---|---|---|---|
| 7. | 7 + 5 + 4 | 10. | 2 + 5 + 7 |
| 8. | 6 + 2 + 3 | 11. | 4 + 5 + 8 |
| 9. | 1 + 8 + 4 | 12. | 9 + 8 + 1 |

Find the 11, then the answer (add 10 and adjust):

| | | | |
|---|---|---|---|
| 13. | 3 + 8 + 9 | 15. | 6 + 2 + 9 |
| 14. | 4 + 4 + 7 | 16. | 6 + 8 + 5 |

A mixture:

| | | | |
|---|---|---|---|
| 17. | 2 + 5 + 8 | 19. | 5 + 7 + 2 |
| 18. | 6 + 5 + 7 | 20. | 10 + 1 + 6 |

**Answers**

1. 18
2. 12
3. 19
4. 13
5. 16
6. 14
7. 16
8. 11
9. 13
10. 14
11. 17
12. 18
13. 20
14. 15
15. 17
16. 19
17. 15
18. 18
19. 14
20. 17

**SCHOLASTIC**

# Missing numbers

Find the third number (for example *If three numbers total 12 and two of them are 6 and 4, what is the third number?*)

1. Total 16    3 + 8 + ☐          5. Total 20    8 + 3 + ☐

2. Total 10    2 + 5 + ☐          6. Total 14    6 + 2 + ☐

3. Total 18    9 + 6 + ☐          7. Total 19    7 + 8 + ☐

4. Total 15    1 + 9 + ☐          8. Total 20    9 + 4 + ☐

Find the fourth number.

9.    8 + 2 + 6 + ☐ = 18          13. 8 + 5 + 6 + ☐ = 30

10.   7 + 4 + 8 + ☐ = 24          14. 7 + 1 + 3 + ☐ = 23

11.   6 + 8 + 3 + ☐ = 21          15. 3 + 7 + 8 + ☐ = 25

12.   9 + 2 + 9 + ☐ = 27          16. 1 + 9 + 9 + ☐ = 22

**Starter activity 84**

**Objective**
Add three or four small numbers, finding pairs totalling 10, 9 or 11.

**Answers**

1. 5
2. 3
3. 3
4. 5
5. 9
6. 6
7. 4
8. 7
9. 2
10. 5
11. 4
12. 7
13. 11
14. 12
15. 7
16. 3

**Strategies**
● Adjust the pace of these questions to let the children calculate the answer.

MISSING NUMBER

HAVE YOU SEEN IT??

**SCHOLASTIC**

# Quick check

## Starter activity 85

**Resources**
A board or flip chart.

**Objective**
Check with the inverse operation.

Write 8 + 6 = 14 on the board. Ask how subtraction could be used to check the answer (ie 14 – 6 = 8 or 14 – 8 = 6).

Children raise a hand to give a subtraction 'check' for each addition statement.

1. 6 + 4 = 10

2. 8 + 7 = 15

3. 11 + 9 = 20

4. 13 + 12 = 25

5. 7 + 2 = 9

6. 3 + 14 = 17

7. 14 + 15 = 29

8. 6 + 12 = 18

Write 14 – 8 = 6 on the board. Ask for an addition 'check'.

9. 12 – 8 = 4

10. 6 – 1 = 5

11. 17 – 15 = 2

12. 9 – 5 = 4

13. 19 – 6 = 13

14. 21 – 12 = 9

15. 18 – 8 = 10

16. 14 – 3 = 11

**SCHOLASTIC**

# Quick check

Divide the class into mixed-ability pairs. Ask each pair to write an addition statement and a subtraction statement using numbers no bigger than 20, such as:

$7 + 5 = 12$        $18 - 7 = 11$

Beneath each one, they should write two statements that use the inverse operation to check the answer:

$12 - 5 = 7$        $7 + 11 = 18$
$12 - 7 = 5$        $11 + 7 = 18$

Allow two minutes for this. The children then take turns to read a statement and ask the other children for a 'checking' statement.

**Starter activity 86**

**Resources**
Paper and a pencil for each pair of children.

**Objective**
Check with the inverse operation.

---

# Hit the target

1. 8
2. 5
3. 10
4. 14
5. 9
6. 1
7. 18
8. 6
9. 15
10. 8
11. 2
12. 13
13. 19
14. 7
15. 16

**Starter activity 88**

**Objective**
Consolidate knowing by heart addition and subtraction facts for all numbers to 20.

**Strategies**
• Ask for an addition or subtraction statement that gives the target number as its answer (eg to make 12, you could use 8 + 4, 19 – 7, 11 + 1 and so on).
• Collect four or more statements for each target number.

# Odd and even

**Answers**

(to questions on page 92)

1. odd
2. even
3. odd
4. even
5. even
6. even
7. odd
8. odd
9. even
10. even

## Starter activity 87

**Resources**
A pencil and a copy of photocopiable page 92 for each child.

**Objective**
Recognise odd and even numbers up to 1000 and some of their properties, including the outcome of sums or differences of pairs of odd/even numbers.

Ask: *What do even numbers always end with?* (0, 2, 4, 6 or 8) *What do odd numbers always end with?* (1, 3, 5, 7 or 9)

The children together say 'odd' or 'even' after each number.

| | | | |
|---|---|---|---|
| 1. | 16 | 6. | 349 |
| 2. | 128 | 7. | 1653 |
| 3. | 71 | 8. | 2390 |
| 4. | 232 | 9. | 5817 |
| 5. | 165 | 10. | 24 |

Give a copy of page 92 to each child to complete after brief discussion. When they have finished, recap:

odd + odd = even
even + even = even
odd + even = odd

# Top 20

1. 5 + 4

2. 9 + 8

3. 3 + 6

4. 8 + 5

5. 2 + 12

6. 11 + 6

7. 4 + 9

8. 7 + 10

9. 16 + 3

10. 2 + 4

11. 5 + 6

12. 13 + 2

13. 1 + 6

14. 7 + 8

15. 6 + 9

16. 12 + 7

17. 10 + 2

18. 14 + 4

19. 17 + 0

20. 5 + 11

21. 9 + 3

22. 8 + 6

23. 4 + 1

24. 2 + 18

25. 12 + 5

26. 13 + 7

27. 10 + 4

28. 3 + 8

29. 11 + 7

30. 4 + 13

## Starter activity 89

**Objective**
Consolidate knowing by heart addition facts for all numbers to 20.

**Strategies**
• A rapid recall test. Children raise a hand to answer.

### Answers

1. 9
2. 17
3. 9
4. 13
5. 14
6. 17
7. 13
8. 17
9. 19
10. 6
11. 11
12. 15
13. 7
14. 15
15. 15
16. 19
17. 12
18. 18
19. 17
20. 16
21. 12
22. 14
23. 5
24. 20
25. 17
26. 20
27. 14
28. 11
29. 18
30. 17

# Tables Bingo

### Starter activity 90

**Resources**
Paper and a pencil for each child.

**Objective**
Begin to know multiplication facts for the 6, 7, 8 and 9 times tables.

**Strategies**
● Play 'Tables Bingo' as in Starter activity 58.

1. $5 \times 6$  30
2. $2 \times 7$  14
3. $10 \times 8$  80
4. $5 \times 9$  45
5. $3 \times 8$  24
6. $3 \times 3$  9
7. $4 \times 8$  32
8. $8 \times 8$  64
9. $10 \times 7$  70
10. $1 \times 6$  6
11. $8 \times 6$  48
12. $2 \times 8$  16
13. $4 \times 7$  28
14. $10 \times 9$  90
15. $8 \times 7$  56
16. $6 \times 3$  18

17. $7 \times 9$  63
18. $3 \times 9$  27
19. $1 \times 8$  8
20. $10 \times 6$  60
21. $7 \times 7$  49
22. $2 \times 6$  12
23. $9 \times 9$  81
24. $5 \times 7$  35
25. $4 \times 10$  40
26. $1 \times 7$  7
27. $7 \times 6$  42
28. $3 \times 7$  21
29. $6 \times 6$  36
30. $8 \times 9$  72
31. $6 \times 9$  54

# Double number chains

The children stand in a line or circle. The first child doubles the start number, which is doubled again by the next child, and so on. When a number greater than 100 is needed, that child sits down and is 'out' of the game. The game continues with a new start number.

Start numbers:

1. 5        6. 9

2. 11       7. 23

3. 17       8. 19

4. 6        9. 8

5. 14       10. 21

**Answers**

1. 10, 20, 40, 80
2. 22, 44, 88
3. 34, 68
4. 12, 24, 48, 96
5. 28, 56
6. 18, 36, 72
7. 46, 92
8. 38, 76
9. 16, 32, 64
10. 42, 84

# Half number chains

The children stand in a line. The first child halves the start number, which is halved again by the second child, and so on. The child who says a fraction is 'out' of the game and sits down.

Start numbers:

1. 88       6. 92

2. 72       7. 56

3. 96       8. 76

4. 68       9. 84

5. 64       10. 80

**Answers**

1. 44, 22, 11, 5½
2. 36, 18, 9, 4½
3. 48, 24, 12, 6, 3, 1½
4. 34, 17, 8½
5. 32, 16, 8, 4, 2, 1, ½
6. 46, 23, 11½
7. 28, 14, 7, 3½
8. 38, 19, 9½
9. 42, 21, 10½
10. 40, 20, 10, 5, 2½

# Division Snap

Answers

1. 2
2. 5
3. 8
4. 3
5. 7
6. 1
7. 9
8. 6
9. 4
10. 6
11. 3
12. 5
13. 1
14. 9
15. 4
16. 7
17. 2
18. 8
19. 1
20. 5
21. 3
22. 8
23. 6
24. 2
25. 9
26. 4
27. 6
28. 7
29. 8
30. 9

## Starter activity 93

**Resources**
Four or five sets of numeral cards 1–9 (from photocopiable page 93).

**Objective**
**Derive quickly division facts corresponding to the 2, 3, 4, 5 and 10 times tables.**

**Strategies**
● Deal about four numeral cards to each child. Read out a question. Those children who have the answer on a card hold up the card and say 'Snap'.
● If time allows, finish the activity with rapid recall of all (or some) of these division facts.

1. 10 ÷ 5
2. 50 ÷ 10
3. 24 ÷ 3
4. 6 ÷ 2
5. 28 ÷ 4
6. 5 ÷ 5
7. 18 ÷ 2
8. 24 ÷ 4
9. 40 ÷ 10
10. 12 ÷ 2
11. 9 ÷ 3
12. 20 ÷ 4
13. 10 ÷ 10
14. 45 ÷ 5
15. 16 ÷ 4

16. 14 ÷ 2
17. 8 ÷ 4
18. 40 ÷ 5
19. 2 ÷ 2
20. 15 ÷ 3
21. 30 ÷ 10
22. 32 ÷ 4
23. 30 ÷ 5
24. 4 ÷ 2
25. 36 ÷ 4
26. 12 ÷ 3
27. 18 ÷ 3
28. 21 ÷ 3
29. 16 ÷ 2
30. 27 ÷ 3

# Equation game

Write 3 × 4 = 6 × 2 to show that these two number facts are equal. Ask for facts equal to the following (accept inverses):

1.  10 × 4

2.  9 × 2

3.  10 × 3

4.  6 × 4

5.  4 × 2

6.  2 × 10

7.  4 × 4

8.  2 × 3

Write 6 ÷ 2 = 12 ÷ 4 to show that these two facts are equal. Ask for division facts equal to:

9.  9 ÷ 3

10.  14 ÷ 2

11.  50 ÷ 10

12.  24 ÷ 3

13.  10 ÷ 5

14.  24 ÷ 4

15.  8 ÷ 2

16.  5 ÷ 5

**Starter activity 94**

**Answers**

**Resources**
A board or flip chart.

**Objectives**
Know by heart multiplication facts for the 2, 3, 4, 5 and 10 times tables. Derive quickly division facts corresponding to the 2, 3, 4, 5 and 10 times tables.

Any multiplication fact equal to:

1  40 .
2.  18
3.  30
4.  24
5.  8
6.  20
7.  16
8.  6

Any division fact equal to:

9.  3
10.  7
11.  5
12.  8
13.  2
14.  6
15.  4
16.  1

**Answers**

1. 60
2. 20
3. 200
4. 160
5. 100
6. 400
7. 500
8. 140
9. 260
10. 380
11. 120
12. 40
13. 800
14. 600
15. 700
16. 360
17. 720
18. 440
19. 880
20. 580

**Starter activity 95**

**Resources**
A board or flip chart.

**Objective**
Derive quickly doubles of multiples of 10 to 500.

# Double multiples of 10

Remind the children of a doubling strategy by writing:

$40 \times 2 = 4$ tens $\times 2 = 8$ tens $= 80$
$170 \times 2 = 17$ tens $\times 2 = 34$ tens $= 340$
$320 \times 2 = 32$ tens $\times 2 = 64$ tens $= 640$

Double:

| | | | |
|---|---|---|---|
| 1. | 30 | 11. | 60 |
| 2. | 10 | 12. | 20 |
| 3. | 100 | 13. | 400 |
| 4. | 80 | 14. | 300 |
| 5. | 50 | 15. | 350 |
| 6. | 200 | 16. | 180 |
| 7. | 250 | 17. | 360 |
| 8. | 70 | 18. | 220 |
| 9. | 130 | 19. | 440 |
| 10. | 190 | 20. | 290 |

# Tables Snap

1. 5 × 8
2. 3 × 7
3. 7 × 9
4. 4 × 8
5. 6 × 6
6. 9 × 9
7. 6 × 8
8. 3 × 9
9. 7 × 6
10. 4 × 7
11. 8 × 9
12. 5 × 7
13. 9 × 6
14. 7 × 7
15. 4 × 6
16. 5 × 6
17. 8 × 8
18. 8 × 7
19. 5 × 9
20. 3 × 6

**Starter activity 96**

**Resources**
Two or more sets of Snap cards (enlarged) from photocopiable page 95.

**Objective**
Begin to know multiplication facts for the 6, 7, 8 and 9 times tables.

**Strategies**
• Deal at least one 'Snap' card to each child, who holds it up and says 'Snap' when it is the answer to a question.
• The children swap cards with a neighbour to repeat the game.

**Answers**
1. 40
2. 21
3. 63
4. 32
5. 36
6. 81
7. 48
8. 27
9. 42
10. 28
11. 72
12. 35
13. 54
14. 49
15. 24
16. 30
17. 64
18. 56
19. 45
20. 18

# Times tables facts

1. 90
2. 48
3. 30
4. 70
5. 27
6. 16
7. 49
8. 54
9. 28
10. 18
11. 32
12. 45
13. 80
14. 36
15. 64
16. 12
17. 63
18. 14
19. 72
20. 42

**Starter activity 98**

**Objective**
Begin to know multiplication facts for the 6, 7, 8 and 9 times tables.

**Strategies**
• Ask: *In which times table is 42 an answer?*
• Remind the children that 42 is a 'multiple' of 7 and 6 because 6 × 7 = 42.
• Ask: *Which times tables are these numbers in?* Explain that only the 6, 7, 8 and 9 times tables (up to 10 × each) are allowed.

**Answers**
1. 9
2. 6, 8
3. 6
4. 7
5. 9
6. 8
7. 7
8. 6, 9
9. 7
10. 6, 9
11. 8
12. 9
13. 8
14. 6, 9
15. 8
16. 6
17. 7, 9
18. 7
19. 8, 9
20. 6, 7

**SCHOLASTIC**

# Money tables

**Starter activity 97**

**Resources**
A board or flip chart.

**Objective**
**Know by heart multiplication facts for the 2, 3, 4, 5 and 10 times tables** in the context of money.

**Answers**

1. 14p
2. 6p
3. 16p
4. 10p
5. 18p

6. 18p
7. 30p
8. 6p
9. 24p
10. 12p

11. 32p
12. 20p
13. 36p
14. 16p
15. 28p

16. 30p
17. 40p
18. 15p
19. 35p
20. 45p

Write:    1 costs 6p so 5 cost 5 × 6p = 30p

Find the cost of 2 if:

1.    1 costs 7p          4.    1 costs 5p

2.    1 costs 3p          5.    1 costs 9p

3.    1 costs 8p

How much for 3 if:

6.    1 costs 6p          9.    1 costs 8p

7.    1 costs 10p         10.   1 costs 4p

8.    1 costs 2p

How much for 4 if:

11.   1 costs 8p          14.   1 costs 4p

12.   1 costs 5p          15.   1 costs 7p

13.   1 costs 9p

How much for 5 if:

16.   1 costs 6p          19.   1 costs 7p

17.   1 costs 8p          20.   1 costs 9p

18.   1 costs 3p

# Odd one out

Ask: *Which number does not belong in this set: 12, 60, 36, 17?* (All are multiples of 6 except 17.)

Ask: *Which number does not belong, and why?* The children may need to write the numbers down quickly before answering. Explain that the sets belong to the 6, 7, 8 and 9 times tables.

1.    7, 70, 15, 21

2.    6, 47, 36, 12

3.    81, 18, 16, 45

4.    14, 42, 28, 54

5.    36, 64, 40, 80

Allow one minute for each pair to write four numbers, one of which does not belong. Then each pair should read out their numbers and ask the class which number doesn't belong and why.

**Starter activity 99**

**Resources**
Paper and a pencil for each pair of children.

**Objective**
Begin to know multiplication facts for the 6, 7, 8 and 9 times tables.

**Strategies**
• Divide the class into mixed-ability pairs.

**Answers**

1. 15 (not a multiple of 7)

2. 47 (not a multiple of 6)

3. 16 (not a multiple of 9)

4. 54 (not a multiple of 7)

5. 36 (not a multiple of 8)

# Tables Bingo

**Answers**

1. 21
2. 40
3. 63
4. 4
5. 10
6. 16
7. 81
8. 12
9. 25
10. 42
11. 15
12. 6
13. 30
14. 18
15. 24
16. 32
17. 45
18. 20
19. 27
20. 8
21. 28
22. 40
23. 9
24. 36
25. 14
26. 2
27. 48
28. 35
29. 100
30. 54
31. 7
32. 72
33. 80
34. 49
35. 5
36. 60
37. 70
38. 3
39. 90
40. 56
41. 50
42. 64

## Starter activity 100

**Resources**
Paper and a pencil for each child.

**Objectives**
**Know by heart multiplication facts for the 2, 3, 4, 5 and 10 times tables.** Begin to know multiplication facts for the 6, 7, 8 and 9 times tables.

**Strategies**
● The children write eight multiples of 2, 3, 4, 5, 6, 7, 8, 9 or 10 from their times tables spread out on their paper. They cross out each number when it is the answer to a question. The first child to cross out all eight numbers wins.
● Repeat the game, using the same questions in a different order.

1. $7 \times 3$
2. $4 \times 10$
3. $9 \times 7$
4. $1 \times 4$
5. $2 \times 5$
6. $8 \times 2$
7. $9 \times 9$
8. $2 \times 6$
9. $5 \times 5$
10. $7 \times 6$
11. $5 \times 3$
12. $3 \times 2$
13. $3 \times 10$
14. $2 \times 9$
15. $3 \times 8$
16. $8 \times 4$
17. $9 \times 5$
18. $10 \times 2$
19. $9 \times 3$
20. $4 \times 2$
21. $4 \times 7$

22. $10 \times 4$
23. $3 \times 3$
24. $4 \times 9$
25. $2 \times 7$
26. $1 \times 2$
27. $6 \times 8$
28. $7 \times 5$
29. $10 \times 10$
30. $9 \times 6$
31. $1 \times 7$
32. $8 \times 9$
33. $10 \times 8$
34. $7 \times 7$
35. $1 \times 5$
36. $6 \times 10$
37. $7 \times 10$
38. $1 \times 3$
39. $10 \times 9$
40. $7 \times 8$
41. $10 \times 5$
42. $8 \times 8$

# Shape Snap cards

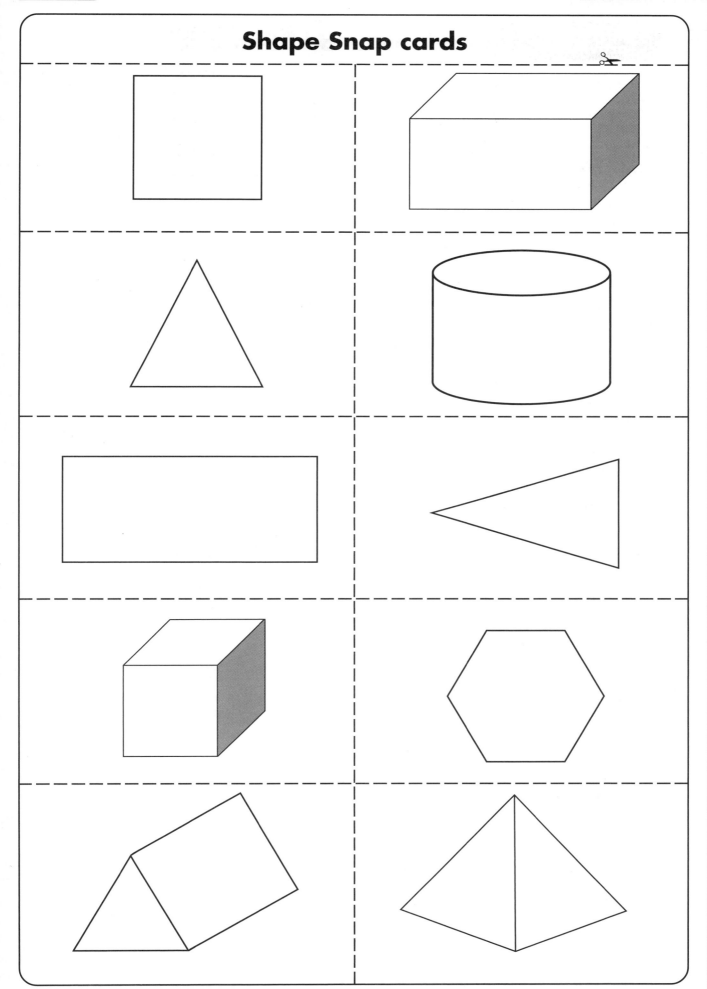

# Odds and evens addition grid

| + | 1 | 2 | 3 | 4 |
|---|---|---|---|---|
| **1** | | | | |
| **2** | | | | |
| **3** | | | | |
| **4** | | | | |

odd + odd = _____

even + even = _____

odd + even = _____

1.  $14 + 11$ = even + odd = odd

2.  $26 + 12$ = _____ + _____ = _____

3.  $17 + 18$ = _____ + _____ = _____

4.  $232 + 214$ = _____ + _____ = _____

5.  $380 + 146$ = _____ + _____ = _____

6.  $291 + 603$ = _____ + _____ = _____

7.  $449 + 256$ = _____ + _____ = _____

8.  $1728 + 1173$ = _____ + _____ = _____

9.  $2062 + 3150$ = _____ + _____ = _____

10. $4295 + 1389$ = _____ + _____ = _____

# Numeral cards 0–9

| 0 | 1 |
|---|---|
| 2 | 3 |
| 4 | 5 |
| 6 | 7 |
| 8 | 9 |

# Snap cards set 1

| | | | |
|---|---|---|---|
| 12 | 14 | 16 | 18 |
| 21 | 24 | 27 | 28 |
| 32 | 36 | 20 | 25 |
| 30 | 35 | 40 | 45 |

Snap cards set 1

**S**CHOLASTIC

# Snap cards set 2

| | | | |
|---|---|---|---|
| 18 | 24 | 30 | 36 |
| 42 | 48 | 54 | 28 |
| 35 | 49 | 56 | 63 |
| 32 | 40 | 64 | 72 |
| 21 | 27 | 45 | 81 |

# Index

Note that the numbers given here are activity numbers, not page numbers.